*Do You Sleep With
That Leg On?*

Do You Sleep
with that
Leg On ?

THE STORY OF ERSKINE HOSPITAL

Foreword by
H R H The Prince of Wales

Harry Diamond

ERSKINE HOSPITAL

First published in Great Britain 2001
Erskine Hospital
Bishopton
Renfrewshire
PA7 5PU

www.erskine.org.uk

ISBN 0-9541259-0-8

Printed by The Bath Press Ltd

Contents

Acknowledgements

I am grateful to the residents and staff of Erskine Hospital, its benefactors, consultants, my colleagues on the Executive Committee, and everyone else who gave me their friendly and willing cooperation in the writing of this book.

Harry Diamond
Glasgow 2001

ST. JAMES'S PALACE

As Patron of Erskine Hospital for the past fifteen years, I have enjoyed a close relationship with a Scottish charity that has a long, and justifiably proud, tradition of caring for ex-Service men and women. Since the Hospital first opened in 1916 it has looked after more than 65,000 former members of the Services.

During my visits to Erskine I have been immensely impressed by the wonderful family atmosphere that pervades the organisation. The unique common bond created by every resident, young and old, having served his or her country in uniform is immediately apparent. The dedication, commitment and true professionalism of the staff not only make possible the high standards of care evident throughout the Hospital, but also contribute crucially to the marvellous sense of happiness throughout this special place.

I was delighted to have made a very small contribution to the design of The Erskine Home - the major project in the Erskine 2000 development which was essential if the Hospital was to be equipped with modern facilities fit for the 21st Century. And I am greatly encouraged by Erskine's determination to be able to provide care to former soldiers, sailors and airmen, male and female, across the whole of Scotland.

Erskine Hospital's charitable work is only made possible by the generosity of a huge number of people from all walks of life. None of this is taken for granted, and I am very grateful to all Erskine's supporters.

"Do You Sleep With That Leg On?" is a moving and heart-warming story of a much-cherished Scottish institution. I wholeheartedly commend it to everyone who cares about the welfare and happiness of the service men and women who have given service, and often made huge personal sacrifices, on behalf of us and our country.

A new beginning

In the year 2000 Erskine Hospital will still be needed to care for those who served in The Second World War and subsequent actions.

The Prince of Wales, the hospital's Patron, wrote these words in 1982, a prediction which proved remarkably, and regrettably, accurate. As Erskine entered the 21st century it took with it the responsibility of looking after men and women who had served their country in one way or another during the most destructive century in human history.

As the new century dawned there were 214 residents in Erskine, including 141 ex-Service people from the Second World War, but it was not to cater for them that Erskine was founded. What was to become one of the most famous hospitals of its kind was started in 1916 in the middle of the first war to engulf the world's major nations.

As late as 1988 there were still 24 veterans from the First World War in the hospital; now there are none. The last one was Mr James Meechan, a former HLI man and Royal Scot, who died in January 1999 at the age of 100. He was in Erskine only eight months but had been in the hospital for four weeks' respite care in 1982.

Fit young men marched off in 1914 in defence of the free world and came back from battlefields of the Somme, Ypres, Mons, the Ardennes, Palestine, Passchendaele, Gallipoli, and from naval battles like Jutland, Coronel, and the Falklands physically broken, without an arm or a leg, or with some other terrifying wound. The carnage went on until 1918.

Only two-and-a-half decades later, on September 3, 1939, another generation went to war again, some to the battlefields of France and Germany, Italy, Greece, the Middle East, Far East or North Africa where their fathers had fought before them.

In terms of lives lost and material damage the Second World War proved to be the most devastating war of all time and since it ended in 1945 there have been more than 90 conflicts in various parts of the world, Korea, Northern Ireland, Egypt, the Falklands, Malaysia, Cyprus, Palestine, Kosovo, East Timor, Bosnia, the Persian Gulf and many other places where their political problems could apparently be solved only by the shedding of blood, and sometimes not even then.

British troops took part in all of these and many of them ultimately found their way to Erskine. In fact since it opened in October 1916, Erskine has looked after more than 65,000 ex-Service people. At Christmas 1999 Prime Minister Tony Blair sent a message to some 90,000 British troops throughout the world thanking them for "helping to make the world a safer place".

Since its first day Erskine Hospital's philosophy has been to provide the highest possible standard of medical and nursing care for its people, to rehabilitate them and return them to the outside world if possible to live a normal, productive life, and if they are not fit enough to do that then to provide a homely environment where they may preserve their dignity, privacy and respect. This ethos permeates everything that is done at Erskine.

For much of its life Erskine had the words limbless or disabled in its title but in 1997 it was decided to drop these references because for so long the hospital's policy had also been to take in ex-Service men and women who had just become ill with the passage of time and for one reason or another could be looked after properly only by Erskine.

How good a job it has done is evidenced in a report by the Scottish Health Advisory Service in August 1996. "In every part of the service we found staff dedicated to the people they serve', said the report. 'This is the essence of a good service".

The report by the four members of the advisory board who visited the hospital in May of that year said the hospital had an impressive philosophy: "We believe that every ex-Service man and woman in our care deserves the quality of care, kindness and understanding that are the direct result of our best team endeavour".

The report covered every aspect of the hospital's activities. On the subject of efforts to maintain the dignity of patients the report stated, "Throughout the service staff understood the need to respect the dignity of individual residents and the important contribution, particularly as ex-Service people, they had made to life".

"Charge nurses showed understanding of the severe loss that residents experience in leaving their previous way of life and home and called for individual care plans to reflect more clearly the importance of the social and psychological aspects of care".

The way residents spent their day was also highlighted in the report. They had a choice of getting up when they pleased rather than according to ward routines; spending the day as they wished, visiting the canteens or attending various therapy departments, using the Red Cross library service, attending the games room with a wide range of activities and entertainment, or going on outings in the hospital coach and minibus.

Prince Charles's comment in 1982 was in his foreword to *The Vanishing Willows*, the story of Erskine Hospital up to that year, by my old friend and colleague John Calder.[1] In this updating of the hospital's story I have borrowed heavily and gratefully from Calder's book.

Prince Charles added that he was sure that with the continuing support of the people of Scotland, Erskine would still be there in the year 2000 to provide the care for which it was so well known. It is thanks to that support and a healthy bank balance that a new Erskine Home with 180 beds was opened by Prince Charles on October 11, 2000 to provide the best possible care for as many ex-Servicemen and women throughout Scotland as possible for as long as the need is there.[2]

The royal visitor told the assembled staff, residents and supporters, "The new Erskine, with its modern facilities, has a very special atmosphere indeed; this is as a result of the unique bond that exists between all the ex-Service men and women and the commitment and dedication of the staff. The quality of care provided is richly deserved by those, both young and old, who in the 20th century made significant sacrifices to ensure that we can enjoy our freedom today. One man I met remarked that he thought he was in heaven".

Prince Charles continued, "The development has been made possible by the immense financial support of so many over so many years and specifically over the last three years for the ERSKINE 2000 appeal. Thank you to so many present today for your generosity. The challenge ahead for the hospital is to continue to raise sufficient funds to sustain the operation; please do continue your much valued loyalty to Erskine".

During a tour of the Home, Prince Charles went into the dining room of Red Cross House where he was introduced by Sister Janice Peebles to several residents sitting round a table. One of the men, former Royal Signalman George Manners, told Prince Charles he had an artificial leg.

"Do you sleep with that leg on?" asked Prince Charles jokingly.

"Not likely", said George, "I would kick myself to death!"

But why build a new hospital in place of one that had done such a good job in its eight decades and gained world-wide recognition for the quality of its care? The man who brought Erskine Hospital into the 21st century, Lieutenant-General Sir John MacMillan, the Chairman, explained, "One major reason was that for eight decades the hospital had been a constantly developing organism. It had spread here and there as we added on bits and pieces in the form of wards and other facilities. Inevitably the time came for us to build a modern, state-of-the-art hospital to meet the highly-advanced healthcare needs and nursing home regulations of the new millennium".

It had also long been the wish of the Executive Committee to extend Erskine Care beyond the central belt of Scotland whenever it became possible. In 2000, after lengthy surveys in the north of Scotland and negotiations with Westminster HealthCare in Aberdeen, it was agreed that Westminster's nursing home, Fairview House in Bridge of Don, would receive a bursary to enable it to provide a number of ex-Service men and women in the Aberdeen area with additional medical and nursing care, physiotherapy, occupational therapy, speech and language therapy, more excursions to the outside world, increased social activities and even a pocket money "top up".

The first ex-Serviceman to benefit from these "Erskine Extras" was Mr John Rainnie of Inverurie, a former Gordon Highlander and Regimental Sergeant Major in the Parachute Regiment who was admitted to Fairview House days before his 80th birthday in November 2000. He served in the army from 1938 to 1961, and was three times mentioned in dispatches.

A similar care package is envisaged with an existing care provider in the Inverness and Dundee areas. Income from a specially established fund of £5 million will pay for the upkeep initially of 30 beds in nursing homes operated by outside care providers.

The metamorphosis of Erskine Hospital, which started life in an 86-year-old house six years into the reign of George V early in the 20th century, to a modern, state-of-the-art care facility in the 50th year of his granddaughter's reign in the 21st century, began in 1993.

For decades there had been major building projects, refurbishments and renovations involving the expenditure of many thousands of pounds. Concern was expressed about the fact that the hospital had never been registered as a nursing home, a fact to which social work departments and health boards had turned a blind eye because of the nature of Erskine's work and because it was recognised that the hospital was working hard to maintain high standards of care without the aid of out-side influence.

Then came new regulations by health authorities, the emergence of the Care in the Community philosophy, and it became obvious that fresh thought had to be given to Erskine's future, its priorities and what resources would be needed to meet them.

A meeting of Conveners and Vice-Conveners on June 24, 1993 recommended that a general planning and strategic review be carried out "to establish general principles on which the future development of the hospital might be pursued in terms of patient care and with a policy that recognised the physical potential of existing buildings…".

Vice-Admiral Sir Thomas Baird, the hospital Chairman, set up a Strategic Review Committee under the chairmanship of Mr David Scott, a businessman and former Territorial Army officer, who was already chairman of the Grounds and Works Committee. The members of the SRC included Mr Michael Blyth, Dr Joan McAlpine, Mr James Scott, Mr Mike Thornley, the Hospital Architect, and later Brigadier Alastair Pearson and General Sir John MacMillan when he succeeded Admiral Baird as Chairman of the hospital. The committee also included senior members of staff, including Colonel Ken Shepherd, Commandant, Dr Tom McFadyen, Senior Medical Officer and Mrs Maureen Lundie, Matron.

With the help of the management consultancy firm KPMG, David Scott's committee analysed every aspect of the hospital's activities and reported in May 1994 that, however much was spent on refurbishments and adding bits onto the hospital in the form of wards and other facilities, these would not qualify the hospital to be registered as a nursing home, and without that, registration funds from the Department of Social Security, Social Service departments, and Argyll and Clyde Health Board would dry up, leaving the hospital open to bankruptcy despite the enormous support from the public and service charities.

The Strategic Review Committee later evolved into an Optional Appraisal Committee, the function of which was to review a variety of options: to retain the existing hospital buildings suitably refurbished, demolish some of the buildings and refurbish others, or relocate the hospital.

Two years later a team from the consultancy firm of W S Atkins Healthcare, led by Ian Tempest and Peter Moir, two architects who were to become involved in all the ERSKINE 2000 developments, recommended that the only way to meet the required registration standards of the new century was to build a new facility. At that time Erskine had almost 300 beds, but Argyll and Clyde Health Board and Strathclyde

Social Work Department insisted that a new hospital should be limited to 120 beds. After much negotiation they agreed to a figure of 180 beds because they believed that more than that would make the proposed new facility too institutionalised, a situation that the hospital itself was anxious to avoid.

It was also decided that the building of at least two smaller "satellite" nursing homes elsewhere in Scotland would be practicable and would also take Erskine Care into the heart of communities where there was a need. The mini-Erskines were eventually located in the centre of the nearby Erskine town and in Edinburgh. They were given the names Erskine Mains Home and Edinburgh Erskine Home.

The initiation of three major building projects at the same time was viewed by a few Executive Committee members with some misgivings, but in all truth there was little option but to go ahead with all three because the hospital could not reduce the number of people for whom it could cater without making provision elsewhere for some of the others who needed looking after.

Five potential sites on the Erskine Estate were examined as locations for the new Erskine Home and the walled nursery garden site was chosen, not only because it was the only flat area of ground available, but it had all of the main services, gas, water and sewerage, adjacent to that site. It was also near the main entrance to the estate grounds, and close to the cottages occupied by war pensioners.

The selection of a designer for the new facility was in itself a formidable exercise. Scores of responses resulted from an advertisement in the *Official Journal of the European Community*, as it was then named. A short list of three design practices was drawn up and Building Design Partnership was selected after a design competition and exhaustive interviews with representatives of the three practices.

BDP were appointed in June 1996 to design the new Erskine. At its peak the full design team, led by Mr Angus Kerr, a director of BDP, comprised seven architects, four quantity surveyors, six building services engineers, and three structural engineers, a total of 21 highly skilled people. The final design was approved in September 1997.

Angus Kerr told me later that the project presented them with a number of challenges which included: to *design* a community for 180 very special people, many of whom were in wheelchairs; to *create* a working environment where carers, administrative and other support staff could carry out their physically and mentally stressful jobs in the best possible working environment, to *encourage* the residents and staff to take an interest in the development and tell the design team their needs and to *place* the building as comfortably as possible within its unique setting.

Dozens of models and artists' impressions were prepared to examine the detailed assembly of the various elements, and to establish the final look of the various parts of the building. The Prince of Wales, whose views on architecture have been known to rattle a few establishment cages, didn't mince words when he commented on the design of the new Erskine. He had asked to see the plans when the new project was announced.

The Prince had had a long-time interest in Erskine since he became its patron shortly after a visit in 1979, and had been back there four times since. He told Colonel Martin Gibson, the hospital's Chief Executive, that the designs were too stark for his taste, that interiors were too high or too low, that the games room looked "factory-like, resulting in an institutional atmosphere" and that there should be some water features outside because they were good for residents.

One could be tempted to think that the views of an interested observer, however exalted, on such a complex operation as the design of a hospital might not be received with great enthusiasm by a director of Britain's biggest architectural design company.

But Angus Kerr said later, "We were very happy to receive Prince Charles's comments. Architecture is one of his interests and he has spent a lot of time studying the subject. His opinions were perfectly valid and for these reasons we did act on some of his suggestions.

It is only fair to say that the Prince's comments were in line with our brief from the hospital executive and were in the pipeline already", said Mr Kerr. "The plans supplied to him were at a relatively early stage in the design development and didn't fully reflect what we had in mind. The Prince fully appreciated this when it was explained to him".

Throughout the entire renaissance period, stretching over about six years, a heavy burden of responsibility rested on the shoulders of the various committees made up of members of the Executive Committee who directed the strategy and policy of the projects, and senior members of staff who did much of the negotiations with outside bodies of consultants, planners, builders, Social Work and Health departments, medical groups and myriad others.

On occasion the work of the two groups, trustees and staff, overlapped, but at all times a spirit of trust and co-operation pervaded their efforts to ensure that everything was done with the least possible upheaval for the residents. For the Executive Committee members, many of whom were at the same time busily engaged in their own trades and professions, their only reward was the satisfaction of doing a good job for the men and women in Erskine's care.

[1] John Calder's father, a Highland Light Infantry man, was admitted to the hospital to be fitted with an artificial left arm only a month after it opened.

[2] The three constituent establishments of Erskine Hospital are all Registered Nursing Homes and will be referred to hereafter as Homes.

A room for
every resident

Erskine Home has 120 nursing home beds, 20 residential care beds, 10 respite care beds and 30 dementia care beds. The design of the dementia unit is among the most up-to-date in the world. The home occupies 34,553 square feet on a 12-acre greenfield site 400 yards from the old facility on the bank of the River Clyde at Bishopton and cost £16 million to build, which sum included all fees for the design team, architects, quantity surveyors, mechanical and electrical engineers, structural engineers, clerk of works and project managers.

All residents are accommodated in single rooms with bathroom, television aerial and telephone sockets. A telephone coin box is also available. A bay window is provided at a level which enables bed-bound residents to see what is going on outside to avoid feeling claustrophobic.

As in the old Erskine there is a comprehensive service available, including nursing, medical, physiotherapy, occupational and speech therapy facilities, a social work department, a library, hairdresser and a banking service, a dentist, chiropodist, optician, dietician and a shop run by the Women's Royal Voluntary Service. Major diagnostic investigations, surgery and X-ray services are conducted externally, usually at The Royal Alexandra Hospital, Paisley.

The move of 400 yards from the old hospital to Erskine Home took about two months to plan and was made over two days, September 14/15, 2000, under the direction of Colonel Bobby Steele, Director of Support Services. It involved the transport of residents (ambulatory and in wheelchairs) and their belongings, staff, medical supplies, and many tons of hospital equipment in a variety of vans, cars and lorries.

It was the biggest removal of its kind in the country and was achieved with military precision and a total lack of emergencies of any kind, a tribute to the hospital team of organisers. The nurses more than anyone else played a pivotal role in the exercise.

A reluctant absentee from the royal opening on October 11, 2000 was Mrs Margaret Crichton, a Clydebank woman, who was at the official opening of Erskine by Princess Louise in June 1917 of what was then named The Princess Louise Scottish Hospital for Limbless Sailors and Soldiers but was later changed to the less weighty Erskine Hospital.

Mrs Crichton was four when her mother Mrs Catherine Gilmour took her to the opening because her brother Bob Livingstone was killed at Ypres and she wanted to see the hospital. "I can still remember the day vividly", says Mrs Crichton. Her own husband was killed while serving with the RAF in 1940.

Mrs Crichton's cousin Sheila Livingstone (Bob's daughter), who lives in Ayrshire, goes over to Clydebank and drives her to the shop at Erskine from time to time. "I always buy something to support the hospital", said Mrs Crichton. "I have a number of things from the shop in my living room. I've got Erskine Eddie, a wee teddy bear. He has a wee pouch for saving money and whenever I go to the shop with Sheila I take Eddie with me and empty the pouch. Whatever is in the pouch I double it and give the money to the hospital. I am always telling people I meet to go to the shop and buy something to support the hospital".

"Sheila and I always have tea in the tea room, too", said Mrs Crichton. It's a lovely place". Mrs Crichton couldn't attend the opening on October 11 but she wrote to Colonel Gibson, "I wish you and all at Erskine every blessing".

In April 2000 the Executive Committee agreed some of the names for the six wings within Erskine Home. Most of these were transferred from the old hospital, where they had perpetuated the names of the hos-pital's benefactors over the decades.

There would be Haig House in recognition of the support from the Poppy Fund and the Army, while Red Cross House would recognise the close association between the hospital and the Red Cross. Pearson House would mark Brigadier Alastair Pearson's distinguished military service and long association with the hospital. Yarrow House would mark the long association of the Yarrow family with Erskine.

The RAF Benevolent Fund recommended McKellar House after Squadron Leader Archie McKellar of Paisley, a hero of the Battle of Britain who shot down 20 enemy aircraft and was himself shot down over Kent and killed in November 1941. Ramsay House was named after Admiral Sir Bertram Ramsay, who commanded the D-Day landings. This was recommended by King George's Fund for Sailors, also generous supporters over many years.

Other names to be perpetuated included Princess Louise (Tower Room), MacRobert Trust (Activities Room), Robert and Edith

McMillan (Library), WA Cargill Fund (Hall), Roehampton Trust (Therapy Suite), Robertson Trust (Café), Reid Macewen (Training Centre) and Compaq (Courtyard). The Dining Room in Erskine Mains would be named after The Merchants House of Glasgow in recognition of its historic support of the hospital and donation of £9,850.

Robert and Edith McMillan left a trust fund to be dispensed at the discretion of the trustees. By an interesting coincidence, Bill Hall, a member of the Hospital Executive, met a trustee on a holiday cruise who had been asked to make enquiries about Erskine. Hall was able to tell him about the hospital's plans and as a result the trust eventually gave the hospital £100,000 in memory of the late Mrs McMillan's brother, Captain David Hutchison of the Yorks and Lancashire Regiment, who was killed in North Africa in 1943.

The 34-bed Erskine Mains Home, the first of the "satellite" Homes, built at a cost of £2.3 million, was officially opened by the Princess Royal on April 11, 2000. Situated in Meadows Drive in the heart of Erskine town, it is near enough the main site, two miles, for the residents to be able to enjoy all the facilities of the larger Home if they wish. They are also near the local shops. Wings in Erskine Mains were also given names from the old hospital: MacMillan, Invernairn, Morton and Logan, the last being in recognition of actor Jimmy Logan's long association with Erskine.

Princess Anne told Mrs Caroline Shotter, Erskine Mains Manager, that she was very impressed with everything she saw, "Despite the fact that the Home is very new it has a warm lived-in atmosphere already" she said. "This is a very special day for Erskine Hospital. The Erskine Mains Home will enable Scotland's ex-Service people to be cared for in a really homely atmosphere." The visit to Erskine was the Princess's third; she was also there in 1971 and 1997.

An Executive Committee minute on the move from the old hospital to Erskine Mains noted that "many of the residents and staff had shown some emotion". Behind the bland formality of these words lay a touching little drama.

Mrs Shotter admitted that she and several others had wept unashamedly much of the morning. "I had been in my ward, Invernairn, eight years, and I couldn't help thinking about the great characters who had been talking about the move in the previous few weeks and had not made it because they had passed away. I felt we were leaving them behind. I was also upset because some of the residents had opted not to come with us".

The people who were moving, and others who were staying behind to wait for transfer to the new main home, gathered for breakfast in the long gallery of the Mansion House, the original hospital building. "After breakfast a crowd formed a Guard of Honour and sang us out of the gallery to the words of the old Gracie Fields song *Wish me luck as you wave me goodbye*", said Mrs Shotter, "By that time everyone was in tears!"

Mrs Shotter has worked at Erskine since 1983, but had been visiting Invernairn ward since she was a schoolgirl of 11. "My mother was a female orderly there and when she was working on a Sunday I went in to help her with the dishes, so my memories of Erskine go back to my schooldays".

There was some good-natured banter, too, at the Long Gallery breakfast. When Mrs Lorraine Ross, Director of Nursing, asked one elderly resident what he wanted for breakfast he responded, "A roll and bacon, a roll and egg, and a roll in bed". Not very original perhaps, but indicative of the "never say die" spirit of the men of Erskine.

Hugh Currie, a former trooper in the 8th Hussars and a Korea veteran, later wrote in *Target*, the hospital magazine: "Now that I've settled in my new home at Erskine Mains, I'd like to thank all the people I miss; the auxiliaries, domestic staff, occupational therapy staff, physiotherapy staff, senior staff, office staff, canteen staff, and residents throughout the hospital who have become my friends over the past 35 years (25 as a printer)".

"It was not until I moved that I realised how much I missed you all. I have to say that the new accommodation I have is absolutely marvellous – out of this world! You will all see this for yourselves come September" (when the other residents were due to move). "The level of comfort you can expect is tops and the care is second to none. You are all free to visit anytime you are passing, the residents and staff will make you more than welcome. Thanks again for all the help and support I have received over the past 35 years". Hugh, in his 70s, revealed that his new home in Erskine Mains gave him a room to himself for the first time in his life.

Edinburgh Erskine, opened towards the end of 2001 at a cost of £4.4 million, has 40 bedrooms in Gilmerton Road next to The Murray Home, an established ex-Service residential care facility that accommodates 36 ex-Service personnel. The Erskine facility serves Edinburgh and the Lothians, Fife, the Borders and surrounding areas. Support services such as catering, laundry and housekeeping are shared with Murray Home. In December 2000 there were already six people on the waiting list for admission. Mrs Jacquie Richardson took up her post as manager of Edinburgh Erskine in January 2001. She was previously with the Marie Curie Cancer Centre in Edinburgh.

Among the supporters of the Edinburgh Home is Hearts Football Club, all of whose 1st XI joined the 16th Battalion of The Royal Scots in the 1914-18 War. Four hundred shareholders and season ticket holders also joined up with the players and together they formed "C" Company.

Another Edinburgh supporter is General Sir Michael Gow, an Executive Committee member since 1989. "I have been for many years a keen advocate of extending Erskine care across Scotland, especially to Edinburgh. Who knows, I may end up there myself!

"I knew of Erskine from boyhood. I was brought up in Edinburgh as a boy and we had many family friends who were in the Army, and it was from them that I first heard of Erskine. Then it was better known in the West than over this side of Scotland (Edinburgh). I did not become directly involved until I became GOC Scotland and from then on I was a frequent visitor with my wife. The more I saw, the more enthusiastic I became".

"When I retired from the Army, after 44 years, and came to live in Edinburgh I asked Admiral Baird (then Chairman) if I might renew my association with Erskine by joining the Executive Council and this was agreed".

General Gow was President of the Royal British Legion Scotland and the Earl Haig Fund Scotland for 10 years until 1996. Both these charities are strong supporters of Erskine, "The Women's Section of the Haig are continually to the front in this support as a glance at the lists of donations show, as are Legion branches", says General Gow. "Talks by representatives of Erskine were regular features of the annual Legion Conference. Quite apart from the ERSKINE 2000 Appeal to help build the new hospital, RBLS & EHFS donations went to the running costs of the old hospital".

Commissioning the ERSKINE 2000 projects – the process of ensuring the buildings, plant, equipment, fixtures and fittings were ready for occupation, as well as preparing the residents and staff for the "big move" – was a complex organisational operation.

Forward planning was essential for the smooth transition and strategies were put in place to make sure every aspect of the New Build projects, from key tasks to the most minute details, was carefully considered, recorded on a commissioning master plan and acted upon.

The commissioning task was carried out by a core team of staff representatives and specialist advisors under the direction of Martin

Gibson and his senior staff. The 10-strong commissioning team met regularly under the chairmanship of Mr David McArthur, Healthcare Development Manager.

Their task was to get everything absolutely right from the smallest detail in the buildings, such as the positioning of a switch for ease of use, the texture and colour of surfaces and furnishings to the major pieces of plant and equipment. Trials of equipment including beds, chairs and baths, to choosing colour schemes and curtain fabrics, were all part of the commissioning process.

A key part in all the new building was played by the Erskine Construction Advisory Committee, the function of which was to ensure that every construction aspect of the three projects went according to plan; that the contracts were properly placed, that time schedules were observed, that the hospital's money was being wisely spent, and that a high standard of workmanship was maintained. The members were Messrs Jim Scott (Chairman), David Ballingall, Graham Webster, and John McIntyre, all chartered surveyors active in property and building. David Ballingall took special responsibility for the Edinburgh project.

The construction committee also felt it worthwhile to rejuvenate the derelict stable block adjacent to the garden centre. A separate company, Erskine Heritage Trust, with members of the local community and hospital staff, was formed to attract grants for a new Training and Resource Centre from Historic Scotland, the Heritage Lottery Fund, Renfrewshire Council and Renfrewshire Enterprise. Disused kennels and a kennel house built in 1857 were also refurbished and form an attractive link with the past, in contrast to the modern design of Erskine Home.

Mr Graham Webster was appointed chairman of a committee formed to oversee the disposal of land and buildings that were no longer needed when the new Erskine became a reality. They interviewed a number of surveyors and estate agents and finally appointed GVA Grimley to advise and negotiate the deal. At one time there were about eight possible purchasers of the site.

Eventually 225 acres and a number of buildings, including the Mansion House, the old wards, Morton Hall, Stevenson House and some staff houses were sold to Mar Estates Limited, a Glasgow hotel and property company.

The Mansion House is to become a luxury hotel with a large number of bedroom suites, function areas and meeting rooms. The ground floor of the Mansion House, whose gallery is one of the longest in

Scotland, will not be significantly altered. All but one of the adjoining wards, which were built later, will be cleared to make way for an 18-hole championship golf course.

The Red Cross 2 day room will become the clubhouse and the Pearson block will be converted to a leisure centre with swimming pool, gymnasium, and some condominium bedrooms overlooking the golf course. Morton Hall nearby will be a modern conference centre.

The developers hoped to include a number of houses in the development. The revenue from the sale of the land and buildings went towards the ERSKINE 2000 projects.

In 1984 The Scottish Development Agency bought 40 acres for £500,000 to pass on to Compaq, the American computer company, to enable them to build a manufacturing unit. This was opened in 1987.

"Relations with the hospital over the years have been excellent", Mr Ken McQuade, the company's Human Resources and Site Director, told me. "We have made good use of the printing shop, and I think at one time some small items of furniture were made for us".

To celebrate the company's 10th anniversary on the estate in 1997 Compaq upgraded the hospital's computer network, donating about £50,000 worth of equipment, and in March 2000 contributed £20,000 to the ERSKINE 2000 appeal. The previous year a jumbo balloon donated by Compaq was launched at the hospital to celebrate its 80th birthday.

The Erskine 2000 Appeal

The ERSKINE 2000 appeal to which Prince Charles referred when he opened the new Erskine Home was launched in 1977. It was the biggest in Erskine's history and its purpose was to raise an extra £5 million to help pay for the new developments.

A small steering group was formed under the chairmanship of General MacMillan to supervise and approve fund-raising activities. Its members were Mr Andrew Dewar-Durie, Chairman of Allied Distillers at Dumbarton, Andrew Robertson, the hospital secretary, Major John Haldane, a member of the hospital Executive Committee, and Ms Angela Harkness,[1] a professional fund-raiser, all of whom were assisted by a hard-working appeal team drawn from hospital staff.

A very busy appeals office was managed by Mrs Nan McCulloch. There was also a need to heighten the public's awareness of Erskine and this task was taken up by Cameron Adams, an award-winning journalist who is now Public Relations, Advertising and Media Consultant. Coincidentally, Cameron's father, Hector, a former RAF man, was admitted to Erskine in 1999.

The efforts of the steering group were considerably augmented by the continuous and generous flow of legacies and donations from the hospital's traditional benefactors like the Army Benevolent Fund, Royal Air Force Benevolent Fund and the King George's Fund for Sailors, the MacRobert and Queen Mary's Roehampton Trusts, Earl Haig Fund, British Legion and innumerable donations from pubs, clubs, schools and individuals throughout the country.

A massive donation of £620,000 was presented by the Earl Haig Fund Scotland from the annual Scottish Poppy Appeal. "We felt the rebuilding of Erskine to be of major importance to the ex-Service community and that it was only right we were the major contributor", said Lieutenant Colonel John Cowan, Chairman of the Earl Haig Fund.

"It is wholly appropriate that it has come from the Poppy Appeal, which is entirely funded by the people of Scotland". Another £300,000 was committed by the MacRobert Trustees, and the King George's Fund for Sailors gave £100,000. The Army Benevolent Fund gave £225,000 in addition to its average annual contribution of £50,000, the Royal Air Force Benevolent Fund gave £200,000 and the Robertson Trust, Glasgow, £50,000.

When the Duke of Kent visited Erskine Home on March 20, 2000 he presented a further cheque for £150,000 towards the cost of the Edinburgh project, £30,000 of which was to help with running costs. The money came from the Royal Air Force Benevolent Fund, of which the Duke is President. He is also Colonel of the Scots Guards and Colonel-in-Chief of the Royal Scots Dragoon Guards. He was so impressed with the main hospital that he told Mrs Lorraine Ross, Director of Nursing, that he wanted to come back to see it when it was completed.

The cheque from the Duke was received on behalf of the hospital by former Flight Lieutenant Robert Kirkwood, a former Spitfire pilot.[2] Although he was too young to take part in the Battle of Britain I am sure Winston Churchill would have been happy to include Mr Kirkwood in the tribute he paid to fighter pilots in August 1940, "Never in the field of human conflict was so much owed by so many to so few".

Mr Kirkwood served in the RAF for five years and started to fly Spitfires in 1943. He flew in North Africa, Malta (he was there when King George VI presented the Island with the George Cross) at the landings in Sicily, and at Salerno in Italy, which he later described as his worst experience of the war. His old squadron, 111 Squadron, still exists at RAF Leuchars in Fife. When he came out of the Service he worked as a sales representative for a bakery supplies firm. He went into Erskine in 1996, although he had spent respite periods there from 1992.

Mr Kirkwood's wife Isobel, a frequent visitor to Erskine, is a retired head teacher who still goes round schools telling the young people what life was like during the blitz. "I also tell them about Robert's adventures as a pilot and about the work of Erskine Hospital, and the children often go away and raise money for the hospital", she said. The Kirkwoods met at the Initial Training Wing at Babbacombe, South Devon in 1941.

A generous donation of £500,000, specifically for Edinburgh Erskine, came from the Garfield Weston Foundation. Sixty members of the 45 Commando Royal Marines launched a £1 million appeal for Edinburgh Erskine by abseiling from the 100-foot high Scottish Life

Assurance Company Headquarters in Edinburgh. The effort lasted 24 hours and raised £5,000.

An anonymous donor in America "with Scottish connections" sent a cheque for £257,000 when he heard about the appeal. And a cheque for $500 arrived in February, 2001 from the Saint Andrew's Society of Connecticut, whose treasurer, Mr John C McNabney explained, "Each year we donate to various charities in Scotland and Connecticut whose mission furthers our goal of providing relief to those in need. It is again our pleasure to be able to contribute to Erskine Hospital and hope that you have a successful year".

Among the many ex-Servicemen's clubs in Scotland who have given money to Erskine for many years is the Tradeston club in Glasgow, whose contributions in the past nine years alone have amounted to £27,000.

Private Scott Geddes (18) and Private Michael McDonald (17) both Royal Scots, handed over a cheque for £10,000 from all recruits training at the Army Training Regiment, Glencorse Barracks, Penicuik. The recruits raised the money for the Edinburgh Home through a variety of sponsored events throughout the year, the main effort being a sponsored ascent of Ben Nevis. Another £10,000 came from artists whose paint-ings were sold at the Contemporary Art Sale and Exhibition in Edinburgh in October 2000.

Stallholders at Glasgow's famous "Barras" Market erected a Second World War shell converted to a giant "piggy bank" and collected thou-sands of coins adding up to more than £2,000.

The Prince of Wales himself helped to swell the Erskine 2000 appeal by donating the entire contents of a cask of 15-year-old Laphroaig Single Islay Malt Whisky to the appeal. The cask, which yielded 260 bottles, had been given to Prince Charles by Laphroaig to mark his 50th birthday. Fourteen of the bottles, signed on the labels by him, have brought in about £50,000 and the remainder were likely to increase that total considerably.

A supper and "roulette event" hosted by Lady Fiona Campbell at Thirlestane Castle, Berwickshire, home of Captain The Hon Gerald Maitland-Carew, raised £5,000. The Duke and Duchess of Hamilton hosted a Wartime Themed Evening in a hangar at the Museum of Flight, East Fortune, near Haddington, and raised more than £13,000 towards the Edinburgh Erskine Home. The sailors of HM Naval Base Clyde raised £15,000 through their annual Faslane Fair event in Helensburgh.

Lady Rachel MacRobert, an American-born bachelor of science graduate of London University, set up a charitable trust after her husband

Sir Alexander, a founder of the British India Corporation, died in 1922. She was left a widow at the age of 38, but this was by no means the only tragedy that befell the young widow.

Her three sons studied engineering at St John's College, Cambridge, and were devoted to flying. The oldest, Sir Alasdair, was killed at the age of 26, shortly before the outbreak of war when his commercial plane crashed as it came in to land at Luton Airport. On June 14, 1941 Sir Alasdair's brother, Sir Roderic, was also 26 when he was shot down by the Germans over Iraq. He was buried in North Africa along with his crew-members. Six weeks later her youngest son, Sir Iain, 24, was reported missing while on a search and rescue mission off Flamborough Head. Neither the plane nor the crew was ever found.

Lady MacRobert reacted to her terrible loss by presenting the RAF with a £25,000 Stirling bomber named *MacRobert's Reply*. Later she gave £20,000 to buy four Hurricane fighters. Three of them were named after her sons, while the fourth was known as *The Lady* and bore the legend *MacRobert's Salute to Russia* in honour of hundreds of letters she received from Russian women who wrote her letters of sympathy. Lady MacRobert died in 1954. Her trust has given more than £35 million to Service charities.

The hospital's Christmas raffle in 1999 realised £34,588.50 and the computer company Compaq donated £20,000 to the courtyard garden in Erskine Mains.

A Royal Tribute organised by the Army to mark the 100th birthday of the Queen Mother was staged on the esplanade of Edinburgh Castle on Thursday, July 27, 2000. Twenty-one Erskine residents were there to see the massed Pipes and Drums and Military Bands of the Scottish Regiments, joined by bands from South Africa, Australia, Canada and New Zealand. The Queen Mother was unable to be present but the Duke of Kent, the Duke and Duchess of Gloucester and Princess Alexandra all attended. The proceeds of £75,000 went to the ERSKINE 2000 fund.

At Erskine the residents watched the televised nationwide celebrations and enjoyed a barbecue at lunchtime. In the afternoon there were entertainers, a raffle, a birthday cake, and a generous whisky to mark the occasion.

As Edinburgh's famous One O'clock Gun was fired that day 15,000 balloons, each carrying the name of the person who had bought it for £1, were released over the city. Mr Hugh McDonald of Campbeltown, Argyll, won a holiday valued at £3,000 because his balloon travelled the farthest, to a beach near Newquay, Cornwall. Mr McDonald chose to take his family to Mexico. The holiday was donated by the Friends of Erskine at Direct Holidays. Erskine itself benefited to the tune of £5,000 from the exercise. A day at the Scottish Grand National weekend at Ayr raised £5,000 for the fund.

Lord (Norman) Macfarlane of Bearsden, founder in 1949 of the Macfarlane Group (Clansman) plc, hosted a lunch in the House of Lords on May 8, 2000 for about 20 people of influence in London who might be considered to be sympathetic to Erskine. The purpose of the lunch was to generate support for a dinner in The Royal Hospital at Chelsea on Thursday, October 19, 2000 at which Lord Robertson was the guest speaker and which raised about £20,000.

Lord Macfarlane has been an Erskine supporter for more than 30 years. His interest began after he was badly hurt during his service with the Royal Artillery in Palestine in 1947. He was shipped off to the nearest hospital and then back to Scotland where he spent a long time in Cowglen Hospital.

"I was never a patient in Erskine myself, but because of the position I was in I did hear a lot about it", Lord Macfarlane told me. "Later I visited two very dear friends at Erskine who were my mentors as my business developed".

One was the distinguished medical man Major-General John (Jock) MacFie of the Royal Army Medical Corps who died in 1985 at the age of 93, and the other was his brother Alex, a retired Professor of Economics at the University of Glasgow, who died in 1980, aged 81. The brothers' home was in Milngavie for many years.

Major-General MacFie was Erskine's highest-ranking soldier-resident (so far). Two weeks after leaving Glasgow University as a medical graduate he joined the Army and spent his whole professional life as a soldier. He eventually became Colonel-Commandant of the Royal Army Medical Corps, and a Fellow of the Royal College of Physicians. He was a Companion of the Bath, CBE and holder of the Military Cross.

One of Erskine's most dedicated supporters is Mrs Mollie Craig, an 82-year-old Gourock widow, who has been fund-raising for the hospital for more than half a century and had raised £53,000 by the time she was presented to the Prince of Wales at the opening of the new Home in October, 2000.

"He told me I had done a wonderful job", she said proudly.

In February 2001 Mrs Craig told me she was still getting up at 5 a.m. every day to make jam, marmalade, lemon curd, tablet, and anything else she can think of to raise money. "People are in and out my house all day long buying the things I make because they know it is for a good cause". She also organises raffles and sales of work, which add considerably to her fund-raising.

Mrs Craig served in the Women's Auxiliary Air Force from 1941 to 1945 and both her husbands were ex-Servicemen and both of them spent short respite periods in Erskine.

"They said everyone was so good to them and they enjoyed their stays there", she said. Mrs Craig's first husband, Mr David Wilson, was an Argyll and Sutherland Highlander for nine years. Most of his service was in the Far East where he was a prisoner of the Japanese for four years. In March 2001 when she received £10,000 from the War Pensions Agency as the widow of a former prisoner of the Japanese, Mrs Craig immediately sent a cheque for £1,000 to Erskine Hospital.

The Wilsons married in 1945 when he came out of the army. Mr Wilson died in 1982. Her second husband, Mr Duncan Craig, served two years as a National Serviceman from 1947 and died in 1997.

[1]Mrs Lizzie Millar, a former Captain in the Women's Royal Army Corps, and Appeal Manager of the Imperial Cancer Research Fund, took up her post as Fund-raising Manager in October 2000 when Ms Harkness's contract expired.

Another new appointment was that of Mrs Jo Chisholm, a former Army Officer, who became Trust Officer with the responsibility of iden-tifying trusts that may be persuaded to support Erskine. Jo has extensive experience in marketing. Her remit stretches all the way to the United States of America where Erskine is registered with the Charities Aid Foundation. Jo keeps in touch with American foundations, companies and individuals on behalf of Erskine.

[2]On July 10, 2000, dedicated the official Battle of Britain Day, 66 veterans of the battle, and thousands of others, gathered at the statue of a seated airman gazing across the English Channel from his clifftop perch at Capel-Le-Ferne, between Dover and Folkestone. Since it was opened in 1993, it has become the memorial to a battle which history decreed had saved democracy for the world. Nearly 3,000 air crew took part in the battle; 544 died and a further 791 who survived it did not live to see the peace. Only 320 were still alive on that July day in 2000.

The casualties
pour in

It was 1914; the year Mrs Patrick Campbell as Eliza Doolittle created a sensation on the London stage when she uttered the words "Not bloody likely" in George Bernard Shaw's *Pygmalion*. Europe was in turmoil as usual and Scotland was still smarting over the rejection by the House of Commons the previous year of the idea of a Scottish Home Rule Bill.

On August 4, the day after Germany declared war on Russia and France, Britain joined the fray. It was supposed to be the "war to end all wars", as many people in Britain tried to persuade themselves, a war which would purge Europe of its many vices. It began in a mood of national euphoria. "It'll be over by Christmas", said the optimists. After all, Britain was then the richest and most powerful nation on earth. The optimists were wrong.

There was an immediate outflow of members of medical and nursing staffs to join the Armed Forces and Ancillary Services. The many recently-qualified house officers who left their positions in the teaching hospitals were replaced for the remainder of the war by senior medical students.

Not only was there a mass exodus of professional and non-professional volunteers; the Territorial Army Scheme of August 10, 1914 transferred to military service from big infirmaries their principal administrative officers, when a general instruction was issued for the opening of all military hospitals in the United Kingdom.

Of the 27 Territorial Force General Hospitals in the UK, four were in Scotland, in Aberdeen, Edinburgh and Glasgow. At the Royal Hospital for Sick Children in Glasgow, the second largest children's hospital in Britain, four of the 12 wards were requisitioned. The unit was designated Yorkhill War Hospital and was administered for officer patients as part of the Military Hospital at Stobhill. In all, over 300 private houses and other adapted buildings were in use within Scottish Command for the sick and wounded.

As the war progressed the casualties kept coming. In 1915, in the first two hours of the Battle of Loos, more British soldiers died than the total number of casualties on both sides on D-Day 1944. On the second day of the battle 12 British battalions totalling just under 10,000 men lost 358 officers and 7,861 other ranks killed and wounded in three and a half hours of fighting.

Roehampton Hospital[1] in London and Edenhall Hospital[2] in Musselburgh, a few miles from Edinburgh, owned by the Scottish Branch of the Red Cross Society, were unable to cope with the needs of the large number of limbless. In the autumn of 1915 there were 2000 patients who could not be accommodated.

The feeling that Scotland should have a large, up-to-date hospital for the service of her hero sons grew in strength, and it was suggested that Sir William Macewen, the eminent surgeon, with his great influence, could render more effective help than anyone else. Informal meetings were held and preliminary steps taken.

While these meetings were taking place the chief operating surgeons in Glasgow, on the invitation of Dr James A Adams, late President of the Faculty of Physicians and Surgeons, met in the Faculty Hall.

The meeting was well attended, and the following resolution was unanimously passed: "That this Meeting of Surgeons of Glasgow desires to express approval of the formation of an Auxiliary Hospital in the West of Scotland for the reception of limbless Sailors and Soldiers, where they may be maintained while their stumps are firming, their artificial limbs are fitted and they are being taught to use them, and also for those whose injured limbs require after-treatment to restore them to functional activity".

A Provisional Committee was formed consisting of the Marchioness of Bute, the Marquis and Marchioness of Ailsa, Sir William and Lady Macewen, Miss Macewen, Emeritus Professor and Mrs Barr, Mrs J F Pollock, Ayr, Miss Anderson, Barskimming, Mr John Reid, Mr David McCowan, Mr H E Yarrow, Dr James A Adams, Major J H Pringle, and Mr William Guy.

The committee then felt it was desirable that the scheme should be launched officially. A deputation led by Sir William Macewen, went to see Sir Thomas Dunlop, Lord Provost of Glasgow, to tell him about the scheme for a hospital for 200 patients. He was an enthusiastic supporter.

Sir Thomas and other members of the committee went to London to see Surgeon-General Sir Arthur William May, Director-General, Medical Service of the Admiralty, and Surgeon-General Sir Alfred

Keogh, Director-General, Medical Service of the War Office, both of whom gave their instant approval.

Then came the problem of finding a suitable building for the new hospital. Several houses in the west of Scotland which were available were looked at and then Mr Thomson Aikman, the owner of the Mansion House of Erskine, situated on the banks of the Clyde, generously offered the committee the free use of the Mansion House and gardens and policies of Erskine for the period of the war and for 12 years after the Declaration of Peace.

He also gave the committee the option, in the event of it being thought advisable, to make the Institution a permanent one, of acquiring the Mansion House and the ground around it necessary for its amenity on payment of the agricultural value of the ground.

Mr John Reid bought the house and grounds, about 360 acres, and presented them to the hospital. Later he acquired an additional 100 acres, which he incorporated into his original gift. The Erskine Estate goes back to the time of Malcolm the Second, the Scottish monarch of the 11th century. Legend has it that Malcolm was fighting for his crown against the Norsemen at the great battle of Mortlach when his life was saved three times by a stalwart green-clad figure who rushed into the melée and scattered the enemy shouting "Eris Skene". The stranger's action was enough to win him the hand of Malcolm's daughter, Princess Cora, and a large tract of land, which he named Erskine after the forester's battle-cry. Despite the efforts of his mysterious protector the bloodthirsty Malcolm died at the age of 29.

Princess Louise, Duchess of Argyll, agreed to become patron of the new hospital to be named The Princess Louise Scottish Hospital for Limbless Sailors and Soldiers. The Princess wrote to Sir Thomas Dunlop, *"The hearts of all of us go out in gratitude and in sympathy to these brave and self-denying men who have been through such peril to serve their nation, and we earnestly desire in some degree to make their future easier for them. Surgical science having made great progress in recent years, it is now easier to provide artificial limbs of such perfect construction that they do materially supply the want. Every subscriber to the funds of this hospital will have the satisfaction of feeling that he or she has been able to contribute in a measure to the comfort of sufferers, and not only that, but towards their future independence and happiness. As patron of this institution I wish you Godspeed in this admirable and humane undertaking"*.

Within a few weeks of the announcement the Scottish public contributed £100,000 towards the new hospital. On October 10, 1916 its

Mr Mark Sherriff, Chairman of Erskine Hospital.

Lieutenant General Sir John MacMillan, Chairman of Erskine Hospital 1995–2000.

General Sir Gordon MacMillan

Colonel David Boyle

Brigadier Alastair Pearson

Some of Erskine's first patients in the long gallery of the Mansion House in 1916.

Sir Harry Lauder meets some Erskine residents.

Captain John Lauder.

Mildred Thomson.

The Face of War

Carving an artificial hand in the early workshops.

Limbs being made in a Clydeside shipyard in Erskine's early days.

Bootmaking in the early days of the workshops.

David Green is reunited with his old army buddy Hugh Currie for the first time since they served together in the 8th Royal Irish Hussars 50 years earlier.

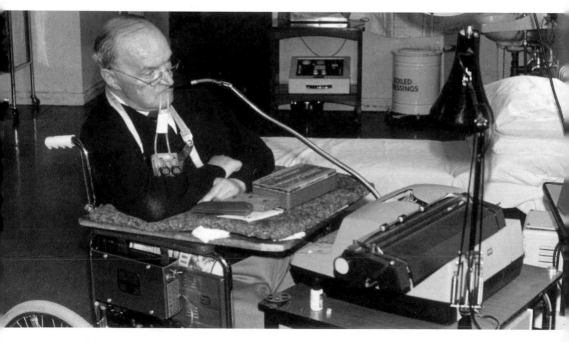

Roddy McLeod with his computerised typewriter.

doors were opened for reception of the war-wounded. The official opening by Princess Louise took place on June 6, 1917.

Mr John S. Samuel, joint honorary secretary, expressed the committee's hope that Erskine might be destined to confer lasting benefit and assistance to sailors and soldiers who had lost limbs in the service of king and country. Princess Louise replied in a similar prophetic note; "The Scots are remarkable for determination and perseverance and never undertake what they feel they cannot accomplish. Here is the result in this beautiful hospital with these beautiful surroundings. Future generations when they see it will be reminded of our brave men of this generation…".

A newly-formed governing body of the hospital was named the Executive Committee, a title which exists to this day. It had 54 members. Lord Provost Sir Thomas Dunlop was elected Chairman and Sir William Macewen Vice-Chairman. Among other members of the Committee were: Surgeon-General Sir Arthur W. May, Surgeon-General Sir Alfred Keoch, The Marquis and Marchioness of Ailsa, Lord and Lady Inverclyde, Lady Macewen, Mr Thomson Aikman, Mr Harold Yarrow and many other men of influence in business, industry, local government and academia.

Four well-known medical men became Honorary Surgeons and two became Honorary Physicians. Lieutenant James Napier was appointed Military Supervisor and the hospital's first Matron, Miss A C Douglas, took up her post. Sir Thomas Dunlop was also elected President of the hospital and Mr John Reid, Vice-President.

The personalities on the list of Honorary Presidents confirmed the importance with which the Armed Services' hierarchies regarded Erskine. They were Arthur Balfour, Secretary of State for Foreign Affairs, Admiral Sir John Jellicoe, First Sea Lord, The Earl of Derby, Secretary of State for War, Sir Edward Carson, First Lord of the Admiralty, Admiral Sir David Beatty, Commanding the Grand Fleet, Field-Marshall Sir Douglas Haig, Commander-in-Chief of the Expeditionary Force in France and Flanders, and General Sir William Robertson, Chief of the Imperial General Staff at the War Office.

The work of transforming Erskine House into a first-class hospital went ahead under the direction of a sub-committee together with a number of committees and sub-committees whose responsibilities covered a remarkable range, just as they do today.

The question of "stimulants" for the patients, for example, was discussed by the House and Staffing Committee on August 16 when the Marquis of Ailsa moved that beer be allowed, "the beer to be of the best quality obtainable", the allowance to each man to be left to the discretion of the medical men in charge.

It was agreed that the Convener, Sir Wlliam Macewen, should communicate with Lord Iveagh (of the Guinness family) as to the best means of obtaining supplies of beer. Sir William reported later that he had been in touch with Lord Burton, another prominent brewer, and Lord Iveagh, who explained that neither of their firms could supply beer or stout owing to the restrictions then currently enforced by the government. Guinness, however, did send a cheque for £26 5s, enough in those days to buy a barrel or two of their world-famous product.

Another committee was charged with the disposal of the hundreds of gifts that flooded in; pianos, chairs, a gong, bagatelle board, billiard table, typewriters, sideboards and other articles of furniture. The Furnishings Sub-committee delegated three of its members to examine and purchase 225 bedsteads, ranging in price from 30s to 40s.

The Gardens and Grounds Committee were promised a cow; the minutes of the Finance Committee on July 17, 1917 contain a formal acknowledgement of a donation of £21 from Sir Mark McTaggart, Bt, to pay for it.

The conversion of Erskine House to its new, humanitarian role pushed ahead as quickly as wartime shortages of labour and materials would allow. There were other problems too; the lighting arrangements were found to be unsuitable and a power generator had to be installed. The mansion was heated by open coal fires and hot air flues; these were superseded by a modern central-heating system. Lifts, a priority for disabled men, were installed. The picture gallery was converted into a patients' recreation room; the old-fashioned kitchen was modernised and equipped with electric cooking appliances and an institutional steam cooking plant.

An operating theatre, dispensary, and Roentgen room were fitted out and the building to the southwest of the mansion was converted into workshops. Throughout the years this was to be a focal point in the work of rehabilitation, where artificial limbs were fashioned, fitted and adjusted with skill and care.

In 1916 Britain was almost wholly dependent on foreign sources for the supply of artificial limbs for the amputees of the fighting forces and the civil population. Macewen felt that this situation was intolerable and with characteristic determination set about changing it. He enlisted the help of the shipbuilders and engineers of Clydeside, especially that of Mr Harold Yarrow (later Sir Harold) who lent not only his yard's technical assistance but also some of its best craftsmen. In fact at one point he arranged for one third of the pattern shop at Yarrow and Company to be used for making artificial arms and legs.

Macewen eventually devised a set of artificial limbs to meet practically every need, and despite the opposition of Whitehall bureaucracy, he succeeded in persuading the Government to adopt a number of standardised designs.

On December 17, 1917 Sir William reported that the number of patients admitted to the hospital since it opened some 17 months earlier was 1,613 and the number of men discharged with limbs was 1,126.

The war in Europe wasn't the only problem that beset Prime Minister Herbert Asquith's coalition government. On April 24, 1916 the Easter Rebellion broke out in Dublin, beginning the Irish War for Independence.

By Whitsunday 1917 contributions to the hospital had risen to nearly £200,000, a great deal of money in those days. By November of that year the Mansion House was unable to meet the demand as a result of the continuing casualties. Emergency huts were built within the grounds to bring the total number of beds available to 400. By the end of 1920, a total of 9,500 patients had been fitted with new limbs – the majority made in the Hospital Workshops.

The armistice to end the war was signed on November 11, 1918, and on that date in the year 2000 millions of people throughout Britain, in airports, railway stations, football and rugby clubs, shops, supermarkets, army camps and even ships at sea, observed a two-minute silence to remember the fallen of the two world wars.

Erskine's annual memorial service was held at Bishopton Cemetery and two residents, Mr Robert Moore, a 78-year-old former Merchant seaman, and Mr Frank McMahon (71) formerly of the Royal Army Service Corps, went to London as guests of the Royal British Legion at the Festival of Remembrance in the Albert Hall. Staff Nurse Allan Chalmers went with them.

---

[1]There are striking similarities in the origins of Roehampton and Erskine. Both were started by people of compassion, imagination and determination. The creative force behind Roehampton was Mrs Gwynne Holford who, in January 1915, found a former Army Private, F W Chapman, sitting at a table in a military hospital with a look of utter sadness and hopelessness on his face. On the table lay two leather sockets as a substitute for the arms he had lost.

"Is this all my country can do for me?" he asked Mrs Holford, who later wrote, "I then and there made a vow that I would work for one object and that was to start a hospital whereby all those who had the misfortune to lose a limb in this terrible war could be fitted with those most perfect artificial limbs human science could devise". The hospital was opened a few months later as Queen Mary's Convalescent Auxiliary Hospital Roehampton after the Queen had expressed a wish to become patron. Mrs Holford worked tirelessly for Roehampton until she died in December 1947.

[2]Edenhall House was the home of Mr William Lindsay Alexander, his wife and four sons. In 1915 Mrs Alexander gave the house to the Scottish Branch of the Red Cross Society after her husband and their four sons were killed in action during the war. The house opened as a hospital for disabled ex-Servicemen in 1921. Four of the wards are named after the Alexander boys, Andrew, Michael, Nicholas and Ninian. Edenhall became a NHS hospital in the mid 1980s with two wards and 50 beds for the long-term care of the elderly.

The Vanishing Willows

It is possible that Erskine would have come into being without the leadership of Sir William Macewen, but it was his formidable drive that enabled it to become a reality so swiftly. When it was first suggested to him that he become the chief organiser he was offered the help of other surgeons. In words reported by one of his colleagues at the time, Macewen replied, "I'll take it up on one condition – that you don't ask other surgeons to cooperate; I am not a cooperator."

This might be construed by some as arrogance; in Macewen's case it was simply an expression of confidence in his own powers of organisation and leadership. He knew what had to be done and he knew how to do it. The conjunction of the man and the hour was seldom more fortunate.

Macewen's impatience with bureaucracy and his skill in circumventing its obsession with the rulebook were legendary in Glasgow's Royal and Western Infirmaries. At the Royal, for instance, he once found great difficulty in getting safety pins for his nurses to complete the dressings after an operation. The story of how he stopped this piece of administrative nonsense is told in *The Man in the White Coat*, a memoir of his early life by his son, the late Dr Hugh Allan Macewen.

The Royal's thrifty superintendent, Dr Thomas, restricted safety pins to one per operation, a needless economy that infuriated Macewen. One morning he sent a nurse with the requisite chit for one safety pin, then at intervals of roughly 20 minutes to half-an-hour a procession of nurses, each with a chit for one safety pin, disturbed the elderly superintendent at his paper work. This went on long enough for Dr Thomas to get the message. He finally capitulated by handing out a full box of safety pins to save him further trouble.

Sir Donald MacAlister, then Principal of the University of Glasgow, told the story of how one day he met Macewen in an outlying part of the University grounds: "He was standing before two old trees of no great sightliness. I asked him what he was thinking about".

"Erskine", he said, "these are willows. We are short of willows for artificial limbs at Erskine. May I have these?"

"I have no objections", I said. "I am sure the University Court will give them to you if you ask for them".

"If you are sure of that, I'll ask afterwards", he said.

That same afternoon the willows disappeared from the University. Sir Donald could not remember that any formal request for them ever came before the court. Sir William Macewen had his own characteristic ways of dealing with emergencies. This story is well-known in university and medical circles and illustrates Macewen's enterprise and determination.

In 1915 Macewen was 67, Regius Professor of Surgery at the University of Glasgow and universally acclaimed as one of the greatest surgeons of his time. He was born on 22 July 1848 at Woodend, on the Ardbeg shore of Rothesay Bay, the last of 12 children. He graduated MB from Glasgow University in 1869; four years later he was a consulting surgeon, and at the age of 28 he became Lecturer in Forensic Medicine at Glasgow, a post once held by the great Joseph (later Lord) Lister, the pioneer in antiseptic surgery.

According to some of his contemporaries Macewen was 50 years ahead of his time. Some of his ideas were in fact so revolutionary as to be unacceptable to his fellows. His achievements however spoke for themselves. He was the first surgeon in the world to remove a lung successfully and that in an ordinary theatre in 1895. The patient, a man, not only survived but was able to resume a normal active life.

Another of his early surgical triumphs involved a man who arrived at his consulting rooms holding a handkerchief to his face with one hand while with the other he tried to unroll a bulky newspaper parcel. The man explained that he had accidentally cut off his nose and had wrapped it in a newspaper "to keep it warm". Once he had thoroughly cleaned the severed nose Macewen coolly stitched it back into place.

In 1873 when he was Dispensary Surgeon at Glasgow's Western Infirmary, Macewen ventured into the field of bone-grafting, convinced that the teaching at the time on the growth of bone was fallacious. He studied how antlers grew on deer; how the antlers when damaged could repair themselves. He applied the knowledge so gained to his experiments in bone transplant but always, before attempting to transplant human bone to human bone, he sought the patient's permission.

Compared with the finely-tempered and ingenious instruments used in modern surgery, Macewen's were comparatively crude but in his skilled hands highly effective. In many cases he used an ordinary carpenter's tools, a hammer and chisel for bone operations and, when necessary, a saw and hand drill.

Macewen's reputation had been firmly established at the 1888 meeting of the British Medical Association when he delivered an address on *The Surgery of the Brain and Spinal Cord*. Nine years earlier he had become the first man to operate on the brain. Later in that year, in 1879, he removed a tumour from the brain and in the course of his long career operated on brain tumours in patients from all over the world.

His address to the BMA in 1888, while mainly composed for the medical profession, gave laymen an insight for the first time into the amazing advance in scientific knowledge of the working of the brain – "the most wonderful machine in the world" as Macewen once described it. Some of the words he spoke at that memorable gathering 113 years ago are still eloquently apposite today:

"Doubtless the dome of thought ought to be left inviolate. The more one saw of the intricate, delicate structure, the greater the reverence one entertained for it and the less was one inclined to disturb its arrangements or to interfere with its function. When it did require to be touched it ought to be with the greatest gentleness, by an acutely sensitive finger, carefully trained by the blessed gift of memory of tactile sensation to which each new impression might be quickly relegated, grouped, and correlated in ordered sequence".

Macewen told a spellbound audience, "Surgery of the brain has its limits, but these have not been reached". *In Macewen of Glasgow – a Recollection of the Chief*, Charles Duguid, a distinguished surgeon who had been a student under Macewen in Glasgow, and in later years a colleague and close personal friend, gives this description of him:

"Those who studied under him will remember him best as the Clinician at the Western Infirmary – the teacher sitting on the high white stool in the spacious corridor between the male surgical and male accident wards... his erect posture, the slight shake of the head that released the pince-nez, the sharp flick of the papers in his hand, and the "ah but" when we strayed in our argument from the path of logical reasoning".

For two years Charles Duguid was present at almost every operation Macewen performed and never saw him at a loss. "As an operator he was deliberate and fearless rather than fast", he recalls, "but no operation was ever performed without the most painstaking investigation and careful differential diagnosis".

More than 100 years ago rickets was very prevalent in Glasgow and indeed in all big industrial cities. Macewen was the first surgeon to devise the operation that was universally adopted to break and straighten the deformed bones caused by the disease. As Duguid observed: "Hosts of men and women have walked erect in Glasgow, saved by Macewen in their childhood from bow legs and knock knees".

There may have been those, sitting on the committees and subcommittees that launched the Erskine project, who found Macewen autocratic. He was certainly intolerant of insincerity and expressed his views with incisive candour. Some of his critics said he brooked no opposition to his own opinions, but in every profession the little men have always snapped at the heels of the giants.

Sam Newell, physiotherapist at Erskine for 40 years, quotes some of the 1914–18 veterans on Sir William's bedside manner: "He used to tell us, in his own modest way, that Macewen and God, in that order, would see us right".

In 1915 Sir William was "the Chief" to every aspiring young surgeon in Glasgow, a formidable figure certainly, but a man of great compassion, as many of Erskine's war-shattered patients came to know.

When he was called upon to lead the great Erskine venture it was as a Fellow of the Royal Society; an honorary member of the Imperial Academy of St Petersburg, the Royal Medical Academy of Rome, the American Surgical Society and the German Surgical Congress.

Honorary degrees were showered upon him: he was an LLD of Glasgow and Liverpool, Hon. FRCS England and Ireland; an Hon. DSc of Oxford and of Trinity College Dublin. He was Surgeon to His Majesty in Scotland and Surgeon-General to the Royal Navy for Scotland. Charles Duguid concludes his affectionate memoir with these words: "It will be a long time before Glasgow knows another of the calibre of Macewen."

The Medical Journal of Australia said of him in 1925, "If great men are remembered more by the fruits of their work than by monuments erected by their contemporaries, then Macewen's great humanitarian achievements place him firmly among the giants of the century".

In 1917 he was made a Companion of the Bath, and in 1922 when the British Medical Association met in Glasgow he was unanimously and with acclamation elected President. We have, fortunately, a contemporary record that does full justice to that historic moment.

In the Bute Hall of the University, in which, almost at one stroke, he had astounded the medical world with his address on the surgery of the brain 34 years earlier, he delivered his Presidential Address before a thronging and hushed audience, which crowded every part of the great auditorium. It was a solemn moment when the majestic, white-haired figure with the quiet but penetrating eyes and the still splendid carriage rose to speak.

With a gesture of apology, for the summer evening was warm, he slipped off his academic robes as if to free himself from all restraint and his commanding figure and voice dominated the assembly, as they were wont to do. Even his critics and those who spoke slightingly of him fell under the spell of his influence and power, although they were slow to admit it and although many of them basked pleasurably in the reflected glory that descended upon them as fellow members with Macewen of the same school. Yet, as the mellow voice floated effortlessly across the Hall, it thrilled many chords of memory and kindled new fires of undying devotion.

Sir William Macewen died on 22 March 1924, almost eight years after Erskine Hospital had first opened its doors. The hospital's report for 1924 recorded his passing in these words: "The movement which resulted in the formation of the hospital was started on the initiative of Sir William. At all times he placed his world-famous skill as a surgeon at the service of the wounded men, and was largely instrumental in the formation of what was practically a new industry in this country, namely the making of artificial limbs".

A striking
establishment

Macewen kept a record of the operations he performed. The hundreds of entries contain only basic facts like the date of the operation, the patient's name, what was done for him, the name of the surgeon and the result. In almost all cases the result was noted as "satisfactory".

The entries start in August 1917 and stop only weeks before Macewen died. What they do not reveal is the cruelty and stench of the battlefield, the agony of the wounded soldiers, the fear and uncertainty in their hearts as they were carried away from the carnage, and the relief when they reached Erskine.

Macewen's operating theatre, always scrupulously clean, and the range of instruments with which he had to work, differed greatly from the modern operating theatre, although Macewen designed several instruments himself for different tasks.

By the end of October 1918 as the war neared its end, Erskine had admitted more than 3,450 men and fitted 2,697 with artificial limbs. Macewen's pioneering work in limb design, supported by a skilled and devoted hospital staff, had already attracted considerable international interest and among the VIPs who visited Erskine at this time were General (later Field Marshall) Jan Smuts of South Africa and representatives of the governments of Australia, Canada and New Zealand.

Erskine was also represented at the Inter-Allied Conference on the re-education of discharged soldiers and sailors and its officials were in constant touch with the training and after-care of limbless men. Examples of some of the articles produced in the Erskine workshops, including artificial limbs, were on display at exhibitions sponsored by the Inter-Allied Conference less than a year after the hospital had opened.

At the end of 1919 Prince Albert (later George VI) came to Erskine to lay the memorial stone of Morton Hall, a new Recreation Centre given to the hospital by Mr and Mrs George Morton of Lochgreen, Troon, in memory of their son George, a Captain in the Highland Light Infantry, who was killed in Gallipoli on July 12, 1915. The Prince's speech was short but eloquent:

"It is quite impossible ever to express sufficiently our thanks to those who have suffered so grievously for us in the late war. But your magnificent hospital at any rate goes some way to repair the damage and to help broken men as far as possible once more to take an active part in the life of the community and so attain what we know to be their keenest desire". The hall was completed and formally opened in 1921.

Boredom was one of the biggest problems confronting an establishment like Erskine where most of the beds were for long-term patients. Disabled men confined to a hospital for indefinite periods must have interests other than eating, sleeping and working.

Recreational facilities were not given a high priority in hospitals in years gone by, and perhaps not even all that much nowadays, but the need was recognised at Erskine from the earliest days and Morton Hall was a valuable addition to Erskine's amenities.

At the end of October 1919 the total number of patients admitted since the hospital opened was 5,532, more than 5,250 had been fitted with new limbs and an additional 2,145 pensioners provided with parts of limbs. "Another year's heavy work has been accomplished" the third annual report noted.

The work did not go unrecognised. Among the distinguished visitors that year was General Sir William Babtie VC, who reported, "Erskine is one of the most striking medical establishments in Scotland and is marvellously successful in its results; it has all the advantages that palatial accommodation, generous contributions of money, and the highest surgical skill and appliances that mechanical ingenuity can provide".

The widespread practical sympathy evoked from the start of the Erskine project was certainly reflected in the generous support of the people of Scotland, but donations also came from many parts of the world; India, Brazil, the Philippines and not least from Shanghai, where in 1919 the Union Church Ladies' Society raised £700 to bring their total contributions since the hospital opened to more than £2,300. In the three years since Sir William Macewen had first rallied public support for the Erskine venture just over £300,000 had been subscribed.

Supporters throughout the world still send money to the hospital. Between 1995 and 2000 more than £52,000 has come from Service organisations, Caledonian Societies, clubs and individuals in many countries including The United States of America, Canada, Japan, Oman, Switzerland, Saudi Arabia, Australia, Monaco, France and Belgium.

In 1919 the Executive Committee thought it appropriate to mention that while they had not made any direct appeal for funds, spontaneous donations received during the year came to the handsome total of £28,919 9s 5d. Erskine's responsibilities, born in war-time, were to be stretched in the bleak days of peace that lay ahead but at the end of the most dreadful decade in history the hospital, its dedicated staff and its growing legion of voluntary helpers faced the future with confidence.

Towards the end of 1920 Erskine went into a period of transition: all fresh "War Office" cases ceased but the numbers of disabled pensioners returning for training greatly increased. In the four years since the first war-wounded had arrived at Erskine more than 6,000 men had been admitted as in-patients. The number of major operations performed in 1920 had dropped to 69, making a total of 470 since the hospital opened.

On February 9, 1921 Sir William Macewen took the chair at a meeting of the House and Staff Committee. Before proceeding to the agenda he submitted two letters: one from a Mr Thomas Hope, of Leadhills, who had been supplied with a pair of artificial limbs and wished to thank the committee for these and for the kindness shown to him while at the hospital.

The other was from the War Office and read, "Now that the Princess Louise Scottish Hospital has ceased to be used for military patients, the Army Council would take this opportunity of expressing their appreciation of the splendid work in the treatment of members of His Majesty's Forces during the period 1914-1920, and would be glad if this expression of thanks, rendered on behalf of the nation, could be conveyed to the staff of the hospital for the excellent service they so ungrudgingly rendered to their country in time of stress and trial".

Erskine's usefulness to the authorities, however, was not yet over. In 1923 the Ministry of Pensions sought its help in providing beds for cases of tuberculosis that had resulted from war service. The Executive Committee responded helpfully, though clearly it had some reservations "Some of these are pathetic cases", the annual report for 1923 stated, "involving constant surgical supervision and prolonged treatment, too often extremely disappointing in its results. They are costly of the service of the nurses and more material things like dressings, and they make a poor show in the matter of statistics, involving as they do the prolonged occupation of beds by the same individuals, too often on to the inevitable end".

But from its formation, the Executive Committee emphasised, it was one of the characteristics of Erskine Hospital that, after the rush and urgency of dealing with the immediate casualties of war, it proposed to offer shelter to men completely disabled, to whom no other refuge was available. A number of beds for TB cases were immediately placed at the Ministry's disposal, the Executive Committee pointing out that, thanks to the foresight of its founders, the hospital's accommodation and equipment were fully adequate to meet this contingency.

A noteworthy record

In 1920 a legless veteran who had gone through the boot-making section at the Erskine Training Centre wrote from the Falkland Islands, "I am still getting plenty to do and am busy with a boot for a woman who has a bad foot. I've never had to use crutches or stop off work since I came back". This tribute to the hospital's work, and in particular to the craftsmanship of the 10 skilled limb-makers then employed, was to be endorsed many times in the post-war years.

"The efficiency and durability of the Erskine Limb", the fourth annual report noted, "has now been universally proved". The report also revealed an extraordinary state of indecision at the Ministry of Pensions over the completion schedules for steel parts for artificial limbs and an equally extraordinary delay in placing contracts for these vital components. "Over a year has passed", the Executive Committee observed dryly, "and although the steel parts have frequently been promised by the Ministry of Pensions, the promise has not yet been fulfilled". The war was over; the bureaucrats were again in the saddle.

Six years after the 1918 Armistice had ended "the War to End War" there were more than 41,000 permanently-disabled veterans in Britain. Nearly 8,000 of them had been treated at Erskine and some 6,400 supplied with artificial limbs. "A noteworthy record", the Executive Committee reported, "for an industry that had to be created in haste". But the hospital's role was now changing; its evolution as a national institution which would provide a permanent haven for disabled soldiers and sailors unfitted for any kind of employment was beginning.

At this period the workshops were providing training for over 100 limbless and disabled men, among them three who had survived double amputation of the legs and two who had lost both hands. Already, however, despite the continued support of the people of Scotland, the hospital's finances were beginning to reflect the bleak economic climate of the post-war years. The accounts for the year to September 1924 disclosed a debit balance of more than £4,400. It was a situation that was to become all too familiar in the years ahead

The Executive Committee began to take the necessary steps to formally define the hospital's role and to enrol it among the philanthropic institutions dedicated to those who had suffered during the Great War. A constitution embodying this object was eventually approved. It would be wrong, however, to say that all was sweetness and light during this transition period in the hospital's life. In the Executive Committee there was a sharp divergence of views as to the importance of the workshops in the Erskine scheme of things.

Sir John Reid, who spoke both as a member of the Committee and as one of the hospital's principal benefactors, held that the workshops were made for Erskine and not the other way around. Mr James M Ritchie, also a member of the Committee, took the opposite view so uncompromisingly that he proposed scrapping the "present complicated and cumbrous system of control by a multiplicity of standing committees" and reorganising the hospital's entire administrative structure. His proposals, however, failed to find the necessary support.

Meanwhile, on the ward floors, in the workshops and in the hospital's other ancillary activities the daily routine went relatively smoothly. There is an interesting sidelight on the cost of living in the 1920s in a report by the Agricultural Department's Instructor, Mr T D Dalgleish. The department at that time employed two journeymen at a weekly wage of 35s each; eggs sold for 1s 6d dozen; a horse, kept in somewhat casual employment, cost 12s 6d a week to feed, an outlay the Instructor evidently thought uneconomic. The Training for Employment Committee however turned down his suggestion that the horse be sold and instructed him to see that it was fully employed.

On Christmas Day 1927 Mr Harold Yarrow made a radio broadcast on behalf of Erskine from the BBC studios in Glasgow. There is no record of the amount it brought in, but over the years, thanks to the cooperation of both the BBC and Scottish Television considerable sums have been raised for the hospital by various personalities. A Sunday nationwide radio appeal many years later by Tom Fleming, the well-known Scottish actor and television commentator, produced a remarkable and welcome £20,000.

In 1927 the ladies of Shanghai's Union Church again demonstrated their support for the Erskine cause with a donation that brought their total contribution to the hospital to £4,224. In 1928 Lt-Colonel C A Gourlay was appointed Physician Superintendent. In the same year the

Annual Report noted with justifiable pride that the value of Erskine-made goods sold in the previous 12 months totalled nearly £11,000, a sum unfortunately insufficient to keep the workshops out of the red, but, as the Executive Committee noted, "the hospital's profit and losses cannot truly be reckoned in a table of money figures".

Rising unemployment in Britain left its mark on Erskine. The statement of income and expenditure for the 12 months to September 1929 showed that, while legacies and subscriptions amounted to more than £4,350, there was a deficit of £1100. Many economies had been made, but these were offset by the withdrawal of a government grant of £2,450 in respect of the workshops.

It was pointed out, however, that disabled men were unable to compete in the open market in the highly competitive conditions then prevailing and that, even under the most favourable conditions, the workshops could not be expected to make a profit. "The subscribers are assured, however", the Executive Committee emphasised, "that we will adopt every means to reduce the loss to a minimum, consistent with the employment of a maximum number of disabled men". It was a salutary reminder that Erskine's great work could not be measured solely in bookkeeping terms.

In the year 1929-30 the Ministry of Pensions decided to close down Bellahouston Hospital which it had maintained for disabled soldiers and sailors since the end of the war. Once again the Ministry looked to Erskine for help: could the hospital provide accommodation for the patients previously treated at Bellahouston? The Executive Committee agreed after negotiations with some of the Ministry's top officials and a considerable rearrangement of Erskine's facilities.

Some of the temporary wards were reconditioned, the X-ray department was brought up-to-date and, very sensibly, some of the Bellahouston staff were brought in to augment the Erskine staff. It was at this point that Erskine gained the services of a man who, with Sir William Macewen, left a light that still gleams warmly in the hospital's annals.

Colonel George Stevenson moved from Bellahouston, where he was Visiting Surgeon, to a similar post at Erskine, in 1929. Stevie, as he was known to patients and staff, served Erskine for more than 30 years with a devotion well above the call of professional duty. As a front-line Medical Officer in World War I, with a Military Cross for gallantry, he had shared the same dangers, privations and beastliness of war as most of the scarred and mutilated men in his care.

Stevenson was a big kindly man in whom the disabled men could confide freely their worries, their understandable anxieties about the future and the frustrations and physical hardship of coping with life without an arm or a leg, and in some cases without both legs. Stevie was never too busy to listen. Mrs Ruth Nevill, a physiotherapist on the staff at Erskine in 1942 and later a member of the Executive Committee, recalled:

"Stevie used to come down to Erskine perhaps once or twice a week and go round the wards. Before he arrived the nursing staff would turn back all the bed covers to expose the patients' legs and feet. At each bed Stevie would stop and examine a foot or a leg or a terribly mangled stump and then very quietly he would say something like, 'well, laddie, I think we'll manage to save this: we'll see how we'll get on but we'll do our best.' Or he might say, 'I'm afraid, laddie, there's nothing we can do about this ... I think we'd really be better with it off'".

"If amputation was inevitable Stevie would explain what was going to happen. He would reassure the patients as to how they would get on, how their artificial limb would fit, how he would see that they had a good stump to enable them to control the artificial limb, and he would have a word or two with them about their home life or the regiment they'd been with when they had been wounded".

"It was this quiet confident air of being in control of the situation that did more for the men of Erskine than anything else", says Mrs Nevill. "It's no wonder that so many of them grew not just to admire and like Stevie but to love him". At one Christmas Day Dinner[1] immediately after the loyal toast someone got up and shouted, 'a toast, a toast to Stevie!' Everyone stood up and cheered. "That was the day we crowned Stevie 'King of Erskine' ", said one old soldier with a chuckle.

Mrs Nevill recalled the spirit that animated the hospital's wards during the Second World War: "Patients were always playing pranks on each other. One of the men once wrote to a Glasgow firm of pest exterminators to say that another patient was infested with vermin of some kind and would they kindly send a representative to the hospital to deal with him. The unfortunate exterminator travelled to Erskine to discover that the patient had a plaster cast infested with maggots, this being an accepted form of treatment at the time. This gave us all a good laugh and was typical of the wartime spirit at Erskine". Mrs Nevill said there were endless romances between patients and domestic staff; one man married the cook, another married one of the ward maids and a third married a nurse.[2]

Colonel Stevenson's son Toby was killed at Arnhem in 1944, a loss that drew him even closer to Erskine. Mrs Nevill recalls that soon afterwards he made a special journey to the hospital and with the duty sister walked slowly round the wards, stopping and talking at each bedside and examining the patients' wounds to see that these were healing. He said nothing to anyone about his son. "He just walked round the wards and then went off again. I think this was just his way of getting perhaps a bit of comfort from the men of Erskine".

Colonel Stevenson died of a heart attack while out fishing in May 1961. On May 10 of that year a joint meeting of the hospital's standing committees recorded this tribute: "The hospital was a place for which Colonel Stevenson had the greatest affection and he always made certain that the interest of disabled ex-Servicemen was given first priority. Among the many duties which he so willingly undertook particular mention should be made of the careful consideration which he always gave to all applications for admission to the paraplegic wards and for improving and increasing the accommodation for these cases".

In 1960 the close and mutually beneficial link which Colonel Stevenson had helped to forge between Erskine and the British Red Cross Society was formally recognised when the society's training centre at the hospital was named Stevenson House.

In 1930, following the minor upheaval at Erskine caused by the arrival of patients and some staff from Bellahouston Hospital, including a number of specialists, Miss A C Douglas, who had been Matron at Erskine since 1916, tendered her resignation. The Executive Committee formally recorded its "very high appreciation" of her 14 years' devoted service and appointed Miss Isabella Hunter, the hospital's Senior Sister to succeed her.

In 1932, just 14 years after the war had ended, the annual report commented sombrely that "age is beginning to tell on the disabled men... it is evident that they are becoming less able to bear the strain of life, particularly under present economic conditions".

In Britain in the thirties, unemployment reached 2.5 million; in Glasgow alone there were at one time 100,000 jobless men; down at Clydebank the rusting skeleton of the giant unfinished Cunarder then known only as No. 534, loomed bleakly over the town. There was no hope for a war-disabled man in the dole queues of the hungry thirties. Thus it was to Erskine that more and more of them turned to find rest and to gather their strength. For those too old and too badly disabled ever to work again it became a permanent refuge.

The years since the war had also taken their toll of many members of the Committee who had first rallied round Sir William Macewen in 1916 to put the Erskine venture on course. In 1932 the death of Sir John Reid, the hospital's Vice-President and its most generous benefactor, was a sad loss to the West of Scotland and the Erskine community.

As the Executive Committee noted in a thoughtful obituary, "Many institutions benefited by Sir John's great generosity. He touched life at a variety of points but nowhere with more gratitude than by those who have enjoyed, and are still enjoying, the magnificent accommodation at Erskine rendered available by his generosity".

By September 1934 the total number of disabled men at Erskine was 157 of whom 51 were permanent residents, 43 were patients, 47 were employed and 10 were members of staff. In addition there were six war veterans enjoying a convalescent holiday under a new scheme started that year. It had been decided to throw open Erskine's amenities to ex-Servicemen, whether disabled or not, who had been ill and who could not afford to pay for a holiday.

The scheme was a great success, more than 100 veterans being accommodated for two or three weeks in its first year. In the autumn of 1934 the hospital's gardens and grounds were yielding a colourful and profitable harvest of flowers, fruit and vegetables; there were bowling matches and countryside excursions – sails "doon the watter" – and in the winter whist drives and concerts. For those able enough to take part there were few dull moments at Erskine.

Meanwhile, further up-river at Clydebank, work had re-started on No. 534, the Cunarder that eventually slid majestically down the ways at John Brown's yard in 1934 as the Queen Mary[3], the biggest ship afloat. It was a great day for the Clyde, the day she sailed down-river for her maiden voyage from Southampton to New York.

A year later there was an even greater day for Erskine. In view of the tremendous public interest on Clydeside in the passage of the great ship to the sea the Executive Committee had earlier formed a special sub-committee to control the crowds who might be expected to seek a grandstand view from the hospital grounds. There was also, of course, the possibility that the hospital funds could benefit from the spectacle.

With the helpful cooperation of the Automobile Association and the Royal Automobile Club, it was agreed to admit the public and their cars to the grounds on payment of one shilling for cars and one shilling for each passenger; pedestrians were also charged one shilling but chauffeurs in uniform were to be admitted free. There was also a special stand for hospital patients and their friends. In the event several hundred people shepherded by 20 policemen (at ten shillings a head) thronged the Erskine precincts on March 24, 1936 to watch the Queen Mary make its progress into history.

The hospital accounts for that year do not disclose the revenue from this one-off exercise but there was an extraordinary sequel to it. With their customary vigilance the Inland Revenue queried the receipts from "Queen Mary Day", claiming that these could not be treated as the ordinary revenue of a charity and would therefore be assessed for tax purposes at the sum of £53 11s. The hospital auditors, with understandable indignation, appealed against this imposition and wisely the Chief Inspector of Taxes in Edinburgh upheld the appeal.

In 1935 there was a further addition to the Erskine community. Following the completion of negotiations between the Executive Committee and the Scottish branch of the British Red Cross Society, patients at Ralston Hospital, most of them paraplegics, were transferred to Erskine. To meet Ministry of Pensions requirements a special paraplegic section was formed at Erskine to accommodate the men from Ralston; four members of the Red Cross Committee were also appointed to Erskine's Executive Committee

In April 1936 Winston Churchill, then in the political wilderness, rose from the government back benches to put a question to the Chancellor of the Exchequer, Neville Chamberlain: "Was he aware that the expenditure by Germany upon purposes directly and indirectly concerned with military preparations including strategic roads, might well have amounted to the equivalent of £800 million during the calendar year 1935; and whether this rate of expenditure seemed to be continuing in the current (1936) calendar year?"

Mr Chamberlain replied that he saw no reason to think that the figure was necessarily excessive. Once again Germany, under Adolf Hitler, was threatening the peace of Europe. At Erskine the old soldiers read their papers, listened to the wireless and shook their heads. So, in the committee meetings, did the men and women who had helped shape Erskine's path, many of whom had watched the first of the mutilated men returning from the shambles of the Western Front 20 years before.

In April 1936 a sub-committee met under the chairmanship of Sir Harold Yarrow. Its remit was to consider extending the use of the hospital and its facilities and the minutes of the meeting throw a revealing light on the concern the Erskine authorities constantly felt for the men in their care and the dedication with which they strove to give it practical expression.

On the recommendation of Colonel C A Gourlay, the Physician Superintendent, it was agreed for example that butter should be issued to everyone in the hospital instead of margarine, at an estimated cost of £100 per annum; that £50 be spent on new books for the library and £20 per annum on weekly and monthly magazines; that new suits be issued to the permanent residents when the Physician Superintendent deemed these to be necessary; and that every man in the hospital be given an increase in pocket money to bring it up to five shillings a week.

Viewed from today's comparative affluence these small mercies may seem to reflect harshly on a system which made severely disabled men largely dependent on public charity and even more unfavourably on a nation which flaunted its poppies on Remembrance Day and forgot about its war heroes for the rest of the year. But as the lists of legacies and subscriptions appended to the annual reports reveal there were many in whom Erskine's humanitarian mission touched a sympathetic chord. In the year to September 30, 1936 legacies and subscriptions totalled more than £12,400.

The Executive Committee, recording their thanks to all individuals and organisations who had contributed to the hospital funds noted that some of the subscribers had faithfully supported Erskine since 1916. Among the gifts received in 1937 was one of £2,000 from Sir D J Cargill McCowan and his sister, Mrs Bonnar, in memory of the long association of their parents Sir David and Lady Cargill with Erskine.

Sir David, Vice-President and Chairman of the Executive Committee, who died in May 1937, was present at the public meeting which launched the Erskine project in 1916, and for 10 years was Honorary Treasurer and Convener of the Finance Committee. In this capacity he was largely responsible for successfully guiding Erskine's finances in the hospital's early years.

In the meantime the abdication of Edward VIII and the ceremonial and pageantry of the Coronation in May 1937 of his brother, George VI, provided a diversion, if only temporarily, from the ominous clouds looming over Europe. Hitler had already marched into the Rhineland, demilitarised under the Versailles Peace Treaty of 1919. In March 1938 he sent his mechanised divisions into Austria; in September 1938 came the "Munich Crisis" when Chamberlain, now Prime Minister, bought a few precarious months of peace at a shameful price: the sacrifice of Czechoslovakia.

At Erskine staff and patients gathered round the wireless to hear his broadcast to the nation: "How horrible, fantastic, incredible it is",

Chamberlain declared, "that we should be digging trenches and trying on gas-masks here because of a quarrel in a far-off country of which we know nothing!" And to none was it more horrible and incredible than to the 222 war-disabled men under Erskine's roof at that time. So Erskine, in common with other hospitals throughout Britain, put itself in readiness for the grim days ahead. The converted mansion had been built in the days when solidity in design and construction was the vogue; it was thus fortunate in having a large basement with spacious passages, which was swiftly adapted for use as an air raid shelter.

The staff were fully trained to cope with all major emergencies; gas-proof rooms were constructed for the use of patients unable to use respirators and black-out blinds required for the scores of windows in the main building were made in the workshops. As an additional precaution the Executive Committee decided that in view of the number of helpless patients at the hospital it would be essential to have male orderlies on the spot at all times.

When on Sunday morning, September 3, 1939, Prime Minister Neville Chamberlain informed the nation that we were already at war, Erskine was fully mobilised to meet its new responsibilities, as it had done 23 years before. Shortly after the outbreak of hostilities the hospital was informed by the Ministry of Pensions that it would be expected to deal at an early stage with wounded Servicemen and plans for extra accommodation, including the renovation of the World War I huts, which had been unused for the previous 13 years, were swiftly put into effect.

The Director General of Medical Services travelled from London to satisfy himself that Erskine was ready to take its place in Britain's front line. It was.

---

[1] The Christmas Day dinners have been donated in turn for more than 30 years by the Merchants House of Glasgow, The Trades House, and the Cargill Trust.

[2] The statutory body that regulates nursing in Britain, the United Kingdom Central Council for Nursing, Midwifery and Health Visiting (UKCC) has in recent years issued guidelines on the subject of practitioner-client (patient) relationships, which may seem to discourage marriage between the two. "Nurses must very carefully consider whether it is ever appropriate to have anything other than a purely professional relationship with a client or former client. Personal relationships with vulnerable clients are never acceptable".

It could be argued that patients in hospital are always vulnerable or they wouldn't be there, but it has already been demonstrated that Erskine is different from other hospitals and has its own ways of ensuring that the interests of patients and staff are always scrupulously and conscientiously safeguarded.

[3] The ship has been moored in the harbour of Long Beach, California, since 1969 and functions as a maritime museum, convention centre and hotel. Its French rival the Normandie burned at the dock in New York in February 1942 while being refitted as a troopship.

America comes
into the war

On November 12, 1939, just over two months after the outbreak of World War II, 30 be-medalled Erskine veterans of the 1914-1918 war paraded at a Remembrance Day service at the Clark Town Hall in Paisley at the invitation of the local branch of the Royal British Legion Scotland. Two days later a similar number were entertained to lunch in Glasgow's Grosvenor Restaurant by members of the Glasgow Rotary Club and were later taken to a matinee in the Regal Cinema.

The House and Workshops Committee reported that, as a result of fowl paralysis and stock moulting, egg production had dropped, and an echo of the first major upheaval on the home front in Britain came from the workshops' boot-repairing department where the number of school boots being repaired had dropped because of the number of children who had been evacuated. So far the war, apart from the nightly routine of the blackout, had as yet failed to disturb hospital life.

In December 1939 the death occurred of Princess Louise, Duchess of Argyll, Erskine's patron and from its inception one of the hospital's most enthusiastic supporters. In a tribute to her abiding interest in the affairs of the hospital and the welfare of its patients (in her will Princess Louise left Erskine a legacy of £1,000 which she directed go towards the hospital's endowment fund) the Executive Committee disclosed that on her frequent visits to Erskine, Princess Louise had often offered "practical advice" on a variety of matters, for as a daughter (the fourth) of Queen Victoria she took her public duties seriously.

A Service of Remembrance for her life and works, in Erskine Parish Church on December 12, was attended by representatives of the Executive Committee and a large number of patients and staff. The silver casket presented to the Princess at the inauguration ceremony at Erskine in 1917 was later returned to the hospital by the Duke of Kent as a memento of the royal patron's intimate connection with the sanctuary to which she had given her name.

In a "Loyal Address" to the King, expressing the Erskine community's sympathy, Lord Provost Pat (later Sir Pat) Dollan, the Hospital's President, also took the opportunity of reminding His Majesty of Erskine's part in the war effort. "The Committee are gratified to record that with the approval of Your Majesty's Minister of Pensions they have brought the accommodation in the hospital up to date and have been able to make available, for use as soon as required, 200 beds for seriously wounded sailors, soldiers and airmen in addition to the accommodation already occupied by over 100 cases of men grievously wounded and disabled from the last war who have made the hospital at Erskine their permanent home".

This was the period of the "Twilight War", an expressive phrase coined by Prime Minister Neville Chamberlain to describe the lull that followed Hitler's onslaught on Poland. The French army remained motionless on the Western Front; the British Expeditionary Force, which had landed in France early in September 1939, was at its appointed battle-stations; the war in the air had not yet begun. As Churchill put it: "We contented ourselves with dropping pamphlets to rouse the Germans to a higher morality".

In the meantime sand-bagged Britain carried on. At Erskine the hospital's devoted band of supporters continued their good work. The indefatigable girl workers of Ferguslie & Anchor Mills organised whist drives, dances and concerts, the Fishmongers' Company again provided the Christmas dinner and Glasgow's Alhambra Theatre made its usual welcome allocation of free seats for the men of Erskine throughout the year.

Early in the war a delegation from the Ministry of Pensions headed by the Minister, Sir Walter Womersley, MP, came north to inspect Erskine's emergency arrangements. They found everything ready for immediate use, but, emergency or not, the Whitehall bureaucrats were still keeping a tight grip on the civilian front.

In March 1940 Colonel Harvie Anderson, Secretary and Acting Treasurer, reported to a joint meeting of the Finance and House and Workshops Committees that he had applied to the Ministry of Home Security for a grant towards the cost of the air raid precautions carried out at the hospital. To most people this would seem a reasonable request; but not to the Minister of Home Security. Regulations were regulations and (said the men from the Ministry) since Erskine was not an area scheduled in the Civil Defence (Special Areas) Order 1939 it was not eligible for a grant.

It was not, however, until a year later, in the Luftwaffe's blitz on Clydeside, that Erskine's Air Raid Precautions were first put to the test. On the night of March 13, 1941, incendiary bombs rained down on the hospital and its adjacent huts; several windows in the main building were shattered by blast from high explosive bombs but there were fortunately no casualties.

One incendiary, which fell at the east end of the servants' quarters, started a blaze that quickly engulfed and destroyed a number of maids' bedrooms and damaged the kitchen roof. The fire was eventually brought under control by the hospital fire squad with the assistance of the Bishopton Fire Service, the Johnstone Auxiliary Fire Service and a party of soldiers from Bishopton.

At the end of 1940 Colonel T A Gourlay, Physician Superintendent at Erskine since 1928, intimated that for health reasons he wished to resign his appointment. In formally recording their appreciation of Colonel Gourlay's services the Executive Committee noted that his relations with, and understanding of, the needs of disabled men had earned the respect of all at Erskine.

The Committee appointed Colonel T H Scott, late Army Medical Services and a veteran of the 1914–18 war, to succeed him. In the mean-time, the effects of wartime rationing and the shortage of nursing and auxiliary staff threw additional burdens on hospitals throughout Britain, and Erskine was no exception. It was a difficult time for everyone.

At the beginning of October 1941 there were 190 disabled men, including 93 permanent residents, at Erskine. The 200 beds made ready at the outbreak of war had still not been fully used but elsewhere the medical and surgical wards were kept busy. Wounded men were arriving from various theatres of war; from the Middle East, Madagascar, Malta and the grim and hazardous Northern convoys which ferried vital supplies to Soviet Russia. And among the maimed and wounded soldiers, sailors and merchant seamen were a number of civilians seriously injured in the blitz on the West of Scotland.

The war took on another dimension on Sunday, December 7, 1941 when 7000 miles away America was brought into the conflict by a massive air attack by Japan on the United States Naval Base in Pearl Harbour, Hawaii.

By 1943 the tempo of admissions to Erskine was rising: the annual report for that year disclosed that of the 471 patients treated in the surgical and medical wards, 147 were casualties of the 1914–18 war and 324 of the 1939 war. But even under the stress and strains of coping with the casualties of two world wars Erskine never forgot its obligations to those aged and infirm war veterans who possibly had no other place to go.

They were known as "special cases". Two such applications for admission as permanent residents came before the appropriate committee about the time Montgomery and the 8th Army were surging in pursuit of Rommel's fleeing Afrika Korps in North Africa. Both were from old soldiers: one, who had served in both the Boer War and the First World War and at 63 was suffering from paralysis; the other, a widower, late of the Royal Flying Corps and the HLI, had chronic asthma. Both found a haven at Erskine for the rest of their days.

In the meantime, despite the ever-present threat of air raids, the blackout, the shortages and the rantings of the traitorous Lord Haw Haw[1], Erskine contrived to keep its chin up. In the summer of 1943 a party of 90 men from the hospital was entertained at Rossdhu, Luss, home of Sir Iain Colquhoun, by the Scottish Western Motor Club. Outdoor sports were organised at Erskine by the Glasgow Post Office War Hospitals Entertainments Committee. There was a distribution of 10 shillings to every patient by the workers at the Rolls Royce factory at Hillington. There were even lectures by the Ministry of Information.

Britain had survived Dunkirk[2] and the Battle of Britain, the 8th Army had hit Rommel for six at Alamein; the war was being carried into Italy. But there were still those for whom the threat of invasion had not entirely receded. Colonel Scott, Physician Superintendent, reported to the House and Workshops Committee that he had received a visit from the Medical Officer of Health of the County of Renfrew and the President of the local Invasion Committee enquiring if in the event of Bishopton being cut off from the pre-arranged evacuation centres, would Erskine accept their immediate casualties. Colonel Scott, with the Committee's approval, agreed but added a cautious postscript that the arrangement would only be on the basis of the hospital's existing resources.

In June 1944 the Minister of Pensions formally opened a new building, which was to play an important part in the rehabilitation of Erskine's disabled men. Built and equipped at a cost of £5,000, it provided up-to-date massage facilities and a gymnasium; the patients were encouraged "to enjoy what they could do and not to think of what they could not do". The rehabilitation scheme comprised physiotherapy, physical training, occupational and diversional therapy and of course the indispensable workshops. A specialist staff was appointed to join the medical and lay staff in what was to become a highly successful team effort.

It was at this time too that, thanks to the generosity of Lady Invernairn of Strathnairn, the Executive Committee were enabled to proceed with plans for the erection of additional wards for 40 paraplegic cases and new quarters for the 26 nurses who would look after them. The new building, known as the Invernairn wing in memory of Lady Invernairn's husband, the late Lord Invernairn, chairman of William Beardmore, was completed and formally opened by the Minister of Pensions, Wilfred Paling, on 12 July 1946.

The war put a considerable strain on Erskine's finances. At the end of October 1943 the Executive Committee had launched a public appeal for funds to provide further amenities, and in general to further the hospital's primary task of helping men grievously wounded in the service of their country to cope with disablement.

The response, the Committee recorded in 1944, was "very grat-ifying". A total of more than £53,723 was raised, more than £35,000 coming from the sale of whisky generously donated by various firms in the trade and auctioned in Glasgow. Since, in those thirsty wartime days what whisky there was usually vanished shortly after opening time, the auction, the brainwave of Mr Herbert Ross and Lt-Colonel Brodie Hepburn, MC, made headline news.

Even bigger headlines appeared in 1944 when, on June 6, the Allied landings on the coast of Normandy, called Operation Overlord, took place. It was the biggest sea-borne invasion in history.

In 1945 Erskine had been in existence for 29 years. It had been born in one world war (when some sceptics said it would outlive its usefulness) and survived, sometimes on the most slender financial margins, to offer its specialised humanitarian skills to the victims of yet another global convulsion. In 1945 some 150 men from the 1914-18 war shared the surgical and medical wards, the X-ray rooms, the physio-therapy facilities and the hospital's social amenities with hundreds of casualties of World War II. Clearly if Erskine was to continue its great work further improvements and extensions would be necessary in the long term.

A sub-committee set up under the chairmanship of Sir Harold Yarrow to address itself to the hospital's post-war requirements decided, in February 1946, on the following priorities: a two-storey building comprising surgical and medical wards, X-ray and operating theatre units (cost £79,000); a one-storey building housing an occupational therapy unit, a 28-bed convalescent wing and admission section (£33,000) a two-storey building for a staff home (£38,750) and a two-storey hostel for workshops employees (£10,000).

To enable the Executive Committee to proceed with these essential projects a further appeal for funds was made but this time the response fell far short of the target. Britain, after six years in the front line, was war-weary. One organisation, however, did respond magnificently.

The Scottish Branch of the British Red Cross Society intimated that it was prepared to contribute £25,000 towards the cost of a building at Erskine to be named the Red Cross Convalescent Wing. Further donations from the Scottish Branch of the Red Cross brought their total contributions to Erskine to £45,000. In the economic climate of the time this exemplary support was highly appreciated by the Executive Committee.

In the meantime, far from the carefully nurtured tranquillity of the Erskine community whose men had seen enough, things were happening in Europe and America that were to reshape the world. The madman Adolf Hitler, who had brought Europe to ruins, committed suicide on April 30, 1945.

Two days later Berlin surrendered and on May 7 Germany's capitulation was signed at Rheims. It was not until America dropped atomic bombs on Hiroshima and Nagasaki on August 6 and 9 that the war in the Far East ended.

In 1947 the National Health Service (Scotland) Act raised a question mark over Erskine's future. Would the hospital, then in its 31st year, be taken over by the state or would it be allowed to maintain its cherished independence? Sir Norman L Graham, then one of the top civil servants at St Andrew's House, revealed later that serious thought had been given to the first proposition; but following a visit to Erskine by Mr George Buchanan, Minister of Pensions, and senior civil servants, the Executive Committee, which had been vigorously opposed to nationalisation, received a letter from the Department of Health for Scotland, dated 23 March 1948.

It contained good news: "I am directed by the Secretary of State to inform you that he has considered the position of the Princess Louise Scottish Hospital for Limbless Sailors and Soldiers in relation to the provision of the National Health Service (Scotland) Act and has decided that the transfer of the hospital will not be required for the purpose of providing hospital and specialist services".

In their annual report the Executive Committee recorded this historic decision with the briefest of comments: "The hospital will continue to be carried on as a voluntary institution and the Committee will make every effort to carry on and develop further the work which has been so successfully carried on at Erskine for over thirty years". In mainland Europe at this time the "cold war" got even colder.

In 1947, too, the Executive Committee was joined by Brigadier Alastair Pearson, Scotland's most decorated soldier of the Second World War, who was to play a major role in Erskine's affairs for almost 50 years.

[1] Lord Haw Haw, real name William Joyce, was captured in May 1945 and hanged for high treason in January the following year after a trial in London's Central Criminal Court (the Old Bailey).

[2] Between May 27 and June 6, 1940 more than 338,000 British soldiers were brought back from the disaster of Dunkirk in a flotilla of large and small ships in the biggest sea rescue in history. And on May 31, 2000 the Duke of Edinburgh inspected another flotilla of ships in the harbour at Dover preparing to cross the Channel in commemoration of that historic evacuation 60 years earlier.

A major
reorganisation

The post-war expansion at Erskine had its difficulties. There was a shortage of building materials, particularly timber; and while the response to appeals for funds had been generous the hospital's day-to-day expenditure was taking an unavoidable upward curve. In 1948 Erskine's rates and taxes went up by more than £120, the assessed rental on the main building having been increased by £100.

Early in 1949 Miss Isabella Hunter, Matron for 19 years, retired and died in April of that year. At a meeting of the Finance and House and Workshops Committee tribute was paid to her long and devoted service and her warm personal interest in the men who had made Erskine their home. Miss Hunter was succeeded by Miss Catherine C Fleming, RRC, of the Royal Infirmary, Glasgow.

In the meantime, work on the new buildings went on, though not as speedily as everyone wished. Construction of the new Red Cross wing was held up by a shortage of plasterers; but the men's hostel, with accommodation for 36 permanent residents, was completed and occupied and tenders went out for the new two-storey block and staff home.

The Erskine of the future was taking shape. The completion of the Red Cross Block in 1950 was the first step in the creation of the "New Erskine" and the replacement of the huts originally erected as temporary structures during the 1914-18 war and again pressed into service in the 1939 war. That the huts lasted as long as they did is a tribute to the workmanship of their day.

In 1950 Colonel T H Scott, who had been Physician Superintendent for nine years, resigned and was succeeded by Captain John Wentworth Farquhar who, after a distinguished career in the Royal Navy, became Erskine's first non-medical Superintendent. In the same year the hospital welcomed Dr John Murray, an Oban GP, as Resident Medical Officer, a new post to which Dr Murray brought his considerable wartime experience as a Captain with the Royal Army Medical Corps in South

East Asia Command. Unfortunately, Dr Murray died with tragic suddenness after only a few months' service.

After a number of temporary appointments the Executive Committee were fortunate in their selection of Dr James J McCall as Resident Medical Officer. Erskine's unique position as a voluntary hospital outside the National Health Service and caring entirely for disabled ex-Servicemen was emphasised in the 1950 annual report.

Five years after the end of World War II there were many men at Erskine suffering from the effects of gunshot wounds, some cases dating back to the 1914-18 war and an occasional one from the Boer War. These acute surgical cases suffered from bone sepsis due to wounds and many veterans had to undergo repeated operations for this condition.

As the annual report recorded: "Amputations and other major operations (88 in 1950) were still required". On the medical side there were large numbers of men suffering from duodenal and gastric ulcers and others with severe heart and lung complaints. Of the 274 patients treated at Erskine in 1950, 57 were casualties of the First World War and 217 from the 1939-45 War.

Many of these cases required constant and careful nursing to prevent the occurrence of bedsores and other complications. They needed special beds and many had to be hand-fed. New applications for admission (to the paraplegic wards) were continually being received.

Erskine also welcomed, so far as its resources allowed, ex-Servicemen who required convalescent treatment following an operation or illness that might have had no connection with their actual war service. More than ever the aftermath of two wars was proving the vital need for Erskine's humanitarian mission.

On 16 September 1951, the Red Cross convalescent block, which had been completed and occupied at the end of the previous year, was formally opened by Lieutenant-General Sir Gordon MacMillan, Hereditary Chief of the Clan MacMillan, GOC Scottish Command, and one of Scotland's most distinguished soldiers. General MacMillan later became Chairman of the hospital.

At the same time, arrangements were made to go ahead with the erection of the two-storey building designed to take the place of the few huts still standing from the First World War. The plan, for four new wards with a modern operating theatre and other up-to-date facilities, had to be temporarily modified – possibly in the light of the hospital's finances – and in the event the Executive Committee decided to proceed with only part of the building.

In the year 1950-51 the number of disabled men at Erskine totalled 239. The number of female staff, including 44 nurses, was 57, while male staff, including two resident Medical Officers, nurses, orderlies, telephone operators, gardeners gatekeepers, and odd job men employed in the grounds, added up to 67.

The salaries and wages bill in that year came to just over £36,500, while the hospital's food bill checked out at £12,426. Erskine's running costs for the year, in fact, totalled more than £81,300 and with capital expenditure on new buildings and other improvements reached a formidable £166,700, Erskine was expanding, but at a considerable cost. In May 1953 the death occurred of Colonel Harvie Anderson, Secretary and Acting Treasurer of the hospital, whose professional skills, given unstintingly over the long period of 37 years, contributed in no small measure to Erskine's onward march.

Colonel Harvie Anderson was nominated to the Executive Committee and appointed Acting Treasurer on the historic day in 1916 when the project was launched in Glasgow's City Chambers. He was made Secretary in 1917 and continued to serve the hospital in both offices until his death in 1953. "By his passing the hospital has suffered a great loss", the Executive Committee declared in a tribute to his dedicated service. Colonel Harvie Anderson was succeeded as Secretary and Acting Treasurer by his business partner, Major Gilbert A. Rankin.

Another member of the original 1916 Executive Committee also died in 1953: Mr James (Toby) Napier of Drums, whose interest in the welfare of the Erskine community prompted him, during the 1914-18 War, to purchase the Old Ferry Inn and initially transform it to a tea-room, with rest rooms for trained nursing staff working at the hospital. Subsequently it was renamed The Ferry House and was allocated to the Medical Superintendent and later to the Commandant.

When the Erskine Bridge was built in 1972, the house was compulsorily purchased by Renfrew County Council. The Commandant moved to a new house much closer to the hospital in the park and unfortunately Ferry House was allowed by the county council to deteriorate to such an extent that it eventually had to be demolished – a planning disaster! In October 1954 the sub-committee on Hospital Accommodation and Future Policy met under the chairmanship of Colonel C B Sherriff.

The new two-storey block designed to deal with the more acute surgical and medical cases was nearing completion and would clearly involve a major reorganisation of the hospital's facilities. The project was one of the most important milestones in Erskine's history. George Stephenson had earlier foreseen there would have been great difficulty in maintaining an adequate nursing staff at Erskine if it had become primarily an old men's home with chronic bed patients and few acute surgical and medical cases. (At the turn of the millennium this did become the situation, but fortunately the loyalty of the nursing staff has proved Stephenson's prediction unduly pessimistic.)

So, well ahead of the scheduled opening of the new block, plans were made for what veterans themselves called "the flittin". These involved the transfer of surgical patients to the new block, allowing the ward that they occupied in the Invernairn Block to be given to paraplegic patients. Medical patients were to be moved from Red Cross Block to the new building, and the Occupational Therapy Department assigned to the Red Cross Block, which was one of the purposes originally designated by the Red Cross Society when they presented it.

The operating theatre, sterilising room and consulting room would also move to the new block and the accommodation vacated redesigned as bedrooms for permanent residents. The dispensary, X-ray room, laboratory and darkroom would also move into the new building. There were to be upheavals elsewhere; the increased numbers would necessitate new dining facilities, part of the main floor of the old Mansion House was to be converted into dining rooms. When completed the dining rooms were refurnished and decorated through the generosity of an anonymous donor. This would allow the old basement dining-room for workshops employees, orderlies and maids to be abandoned.

In 1955, the various moves were completed with a minimum of disturbance and inconvenience. There were other changes at this time: Sir Harold Yarrow retired from the chairmanship of the Executive Committee in September 1955 but remained as Honorary Treasurer and continued to serve on the Executive Committee. Sir Harold was one of Erskine's founder members whose contribution, in close association with Sir William Macewen, to the creation and development of the first Erskine limbs, was a vital factor in the early days of the hospital's mission in the rehabilitation of the disabled men.

As head of his family shipbuilding firm it was largely his influence and enthusiasm that helped to mobilise the shipyards to get Scotland's first limb-making industry off the ground. Sir Harold was succeeded as chairman of the Executive Committee by General Sir Gordon MacMillan, whose family motto, appropriately, is Miseris Succurrere Disco, *I Learn to Succour the Distresssed.*

In 1955 an outbreak of dry rot in the mansion house was partly responsible for a sharp rise to nearly £6,000 in the hospital's bill for maintenance and repairs and the following year Erskine's upkeep costs had soared into five figures for the first time. "For its day-to-day expenditure the hospital continues to depend on public support by subscriptions", the Annual Report for 1955 noted, "and it is a matter of regret that there was a falling off in the number of these received during the year".

A year later, although there was a deficit of nearly £4,000 in the ordinary Income and Expenditure Account, a record sum of more than £141,000 came in from legacies and capital donations. This, as the Executive Committee observed gratefully, was a welcome addition to the hospital's resources.

In 1956 Erskine celebrated the 96th birthday of its oldest resident, Henry Martin, who had served in the South African War and was the oldest living holder of the Distinguished Conduct Medal. Among those who visited the hospital to offer congratulation to the old soldier were the Provost of Paisley and Major General J A Aylmer Maxwell. Other visitors that year included two VCs, Tom Caldwell and William Angus, who were present in connection with the centenary celebrations of the institution of the Victoria Cross.

In August 1956 it was reported to the House and Workshops Committee that the cost of food for June of that year was 3s 4 ½ d per head per day, compared with 3s ¾ d for the corresponding period in the previous year. Also on the agenda were six applications for admission as permanent residents: five from old soldiers, including a veteran of 83, and one from a 70-year-old former wartime merchant seaman. All were approved.

The committee then turned its attention to a more controversial issue, presented in the form of a recommendation by Major Wylie, Deputy Superintendent, that the pigs and poultry departments should be discontinued, mainly on the ground that they were not employing disabled ex-Servicemen. Pigs and poultry had been a useful part of the Erskine economy for some 40 years and it was possibly with some reluctance and no little argument that the decision was eventually taken to declare them redundant.

Over the years there had always been a close and rewarding association between the British Red Cross Society and Erskine Hospital. In 1956 the society created a centre at Erskine, in temporary accommodation, for the training of Red Cross members, whose services were invaluable particularly at times when the hospital's nursing staff was depleted through illness. In 1960 the Red Cross Centre, known as Kinnaird House, was replaced by a permanent establishment named Stevenson House, after Colonel Stevenson who, in addition to being an office bearer of the British Red Cross Society, was, as earlier described, one of Erskine's outstanding personalities.

In September 1960 the death occurred of Dr W J C Watt, Honorary Physician to the hospital since 1942. Dr Watt had been appointed Resident Physician at Erskine in September 1916 and, apart from a break on war service, was Resident Medical Officer until 1942. When he resigned from that post he continued to serve the hospital as Honorary Radiologist. Dr Smith succeeded Dr Watt as Honorary Physician and Dr David Douglas was appointed Consultant Physician.

Other changes in the hospital's establishment at this time included the retirement, in February 1961, of Miss C C Fleming, Matron since 1949. Miss M A G Cameron was appointed to succeed her. The deaths of Colonel Stevenson and Sir Harold Yarrow, in 1961 and 1962 respectively, saddened the entire Erskine community.

Over a long period of years both had given ungrudgingly of their professional skills to a cause to which they were passionately dedicated: George Stevenson in the operating theatre and in the wards; Harold Yarrow in his unflagging zeal in the early days of the 1914-18 war in organising the Clydeside consortium of limb-makers, as Convener of the Finance Committee from 1926 and as chairman of the Executive Committee from 1940 to 1955.

The Yarrow family connection with Erskine, spanning two wars and more than 60 years, was maintained by Harold Yarrow's son, Sir Eric Yarrow, who succeeded General Sir Gordon MacMillan as chairman of the Executive Committee in January 1980. Sir Eric guided the hospital's fortunes for six years. Brigadier Alastair Pearson, who had previously been Convener of the House and Workshops Committee, was appointed Vice-Chairman under Sir Eric.

Sir Eric was also chairman of the Clydesdale Bank, whose connection with Erskine goes back almost to the birth of the hospital. The Bank has generously sponsored the hospital's Annual Report since 1986 in the face of ever-increasing costs. The Bank's Chief Executive at the time was Mr Richard Cole-Hamilton, a member of the hospital Executive Committee.

A Yarrow is still active at Erskine. Sir Eric's wife Joan joined the General Council in 1998 and was a member of the committee that supervised the disposal of furniture, models, pictures, porcelain, books, plants and other items that were not needed in the new nursing homes. Some items realised considerable sums of money.

In the early 1960s finance continued to be a problem for the hospital. In the year 1961-62 Erskine's rates went up from £3,497 to £7,495. The drugs bill increased some £600; fuel costs rose by the same amount and the Sauchiehall Street Showroom, where the sale of articles produced by workshops had been a useful source of revenue, was faced with an increase in rateable value of more than £180.

The owners of the premises, Associated British Cinemas, who had plans for the redevelopment of this and other properties in Sauchiehall Street, intimated that if Erskine were to find alternative accommodation the directors would recommend granting a deed of covenant for a donation of £200 a year for seven years. As a result the showroom moved to Wellington Street in Glasgow's city centre.

Forty-five years after the end of the 1914-18 war and nearly 20 years after VE (Victory in Europe) Day, the Annual Report noted that the demand for admittance to Erskine continued to increase. "With advancing years", it stated, "old war wounds often give trouble and disabled men require hospital nursing when age and infirmity are added to their war disabilities". It was a familiar story to long-serving members of Erskine's staff.

At this time there were about 60 older ex-Servicemen who had exchanged the loneliness of lodgings for the companionship and amenities of Erskine; and among the 253 patients treated in the surgical and medical wards in 1962-63 there were 25 casualties of the First World War whose wounds continued to give them trouble.

On 28 June 1963 the biggest extension to the permanent buildings in the hospital's history was officially opened by Mr John S Maclay (later Viscount Muirshiel), Secretary of State for Scotland. This was the £80,000 two-storey block, which, with commendable foresight, had been planned some years previously in response to the growing waiting lists.

On this momentous June day the building, comprising four large wards with the most modern medical and surgical equipment, assumed a new identity: it became the Ross Wing, so named in memory of the late Mr Herbert M Ross, who lost a leg while serving with the Scottish Horse in the 1914-18 war and whose benefactions to Erskine during his lifetime were, as the Executive Committee gratefully acknowledged, of unparalleled generosity.

In the same year the hospital's amenities were augmented by the gift, from the citizens of Dunoon, of the "Dunoon Room", one of many gestures of support for the Erskine men made over the years by the warm-hearted people of the West of Scotland. In March 1965 a joint meeting of Erskine's standing committees decided that the hospital's senior official (previously the Superintendent) should henceforth be known as Commandant, with full responsibility for all activities at Erskine and directly responsible to the Executive Committee.

At the same time the Committee announced the appointment of Colonel David Boyle, late Argyll and Sutherland Highlanders, as Commandant to succeed Capt J W Farquhar, who retired from the post of Superintendent in July of that year.

Erskine Pine
goes nationwide

Erskine stopped making artificial limbs in the hospital workshops in 1925 because of a decline in demand, new technology in their manufacture and an increase in the number of specialised companies making them. The workshops did, however, retain the skill to adjust and repair limbs, alongside other training and employment activities.

In the early days there was concern over whether the requirement for both the quality and quantity of artificial limbs could be satisfied by Scottish industry alone. Sir William Macewen commented that the making of the limbs would prove to be "a recreational diversion for those whose creative genius had made Dreadnought battleships possible", a reference to the skills of the shipyard workers whose help the hospital was to enlist.

Nowadays it can cost from several hundred to several thousand pounds to make arms and legs, the more expensive limbs often produced for specific individuals and funded by research money. Arms tend to be more expensive than legs as they have to perform a far larger range of movements, as do the hands and fingers.

Erskine residents who are unfortunate enough to require an amputation have this done in the Royal Alexandra Hospital in Paisley or the Southern General Hospital in Glasgow but return to Erskine to heal. The cost of the operation and any artificial limb that may later be required is borne by the National Health Service.

The Erskine workshops are now concentrated on three main activities; a furniture workshop, a printing shop and a garden centre and coffee shop. Erskine Pine makes a range of high-quality pine furniture that is sold throughout Britain and Ireland by a network of agents built up by Keith Taylor, a former naval officer and Director of Workshops and Training.

All the bedroom furniture in the new Erskine Homes was supplied by the workshops; beds, wardrobes, dressing tables, chests of drawers and bedside cabinets. Keith Taylor takes great satisfaction in the fact that the contract was won in the face of stiff competition from outside manufacturers.

Erskine Print is a well-equipped workshop, which provides a wide range of commercial print services for outside organisations as well as meeting the everyday printing needs of the hospital.

Erskine Garden Centre, on which £100,000 was spent in 2001 on improvements and marketing, now sells a wide range of garden produce, which is bought in. Until the site was handed over for the new hospital the nursery garden was used as a market garden to supply the hospital and to grow produce for sale in the garden centre.

While the workshops have become increasingly commercially focused the limitations of a largely disabled workforce, advancing years, illness, retirements and death among the workers militate against a stable, profit-making organisation and even though sales in the year ending September 30, 2000 amounted to a very welcome £1.2 million, the overall deficit was £259,000.

A new workshop costing £1.8 million and largely funded by the Sheltered Employment Procurement and Consultancy Service (SEPACS) was opened in April 1996, which significantly enhanced joinery, wood finishing and upholstery capabilities.

The official opening of the workshop was to have been performed on May 30 by Mr James Aitken, who was 100 that day, but he wasn't feeling too well so his daughter stood in for him. Mr Aitken died the following year a few months after his 101st birthday.

In 1990, a new main craft workshop was built to house basket and cane furniture manufacture and repair, boot and shoe repair and printing sections. It was part-funded by SEPACS and was opened on 23 September 1991 by Lord Strathclyde.

As part of an ongoing programme to upgrade workshop facilities, SEPACS also part-funded a new Nursery Garden Centre and Coffee Shop, which were opened to the public on April 2, 1993. A major change came on April 1, 1994 when Sheltered Employment became Supported Employment. With this change the Employment Service sought to target the funds available for the employment of disabled workers more effectively.

Disabled ex-Servicemen are still employed in the workshops although those who live in the hospital are now few in number. There are usually between 60 and 70 disabled men working there under the government's Supported Employment scheme. Under this scheme, through which certain grants are made to the hospital, disabled people who do not have a Service affiliation must be employed. If they cannot go outside to work after training they may work at Erskine indefinitely.

Ever mindful of the need to find new opportunities to widen the activities of the workshops, extend the skills of its workers, and attract more revenue, Keith Taylor explored in 1996 the feasibility of making dancing shoes for a Glasgow dancewear company based on the designs of its principal Mr Craig Coussins, but the operation was not a success.

The workshops would have had to buy the raw materials, provide the labour and make the shoes but the end product would have been too costly to the dancewear company. The story didn't end there however. The workshops did make some prototypes and these were shown by Mr Coussins to other manufacturers.

When I spoke to Mr Coussins in June 1996 he told me his shoes, based on the Erskine prototypes, were sold in Canada, Australia, New Zealand, South Africa, the United States of America and many other countries. The shoes also won a Millennium Product Award and were on display in the Millennium Dome in London; in addition the London Science Museum had made the shoes part of their permanent collection as one of the most innovative designs of the 20th century.

The Erskine workshops are a further example, if any were needed, of the imagination and foresight of the Erskine founders. Macewen and his colleagues realised the importance of retraining disabled men to do different jobs from the ones they had before so that, if possible they could earn their own living and regain their independence and dignity.

The concept of workshops was discussed at a public meeting in Glasgow City Chambers in March 1916. One person in the audience not overburdened with the same degree of commitment suggested that vocational training should be left to the Disabled Sailors and Soldiers Help Society but that argument collapsed in ruins when it was pointed out that the society did not have a vocational training workshop.

The first workshop was set up in 1917 with the long-term aim of putting each disabled man into employment "best suited to his ability and the nature of his disablement". It was housed in a substantial building in the hospital grounds, which was formerly used for religious and philanthropic meetings by the late Lord Blantyre, whose family had bought the Erskine mansion and its grounds in 1703.

The workshop was divided into three sections: one devoted to the construction and adjustment of artificial limbs; another with two weaving looms; and a third with up-to-date woodworking machines, a turning lathe and planing machine where the disabled men turned out model yachts, chicken coops and all kinds of woodwork.

Basket-making was also taught. A boot-making unit, started under the supervision of Mr R G Allan, a well-known Scottish bootmaker, specialised in boot and shoe repairing, a craft then badly hit by a wartime shortage of skilled men. The wages earned by the Erskine bootmakers after a fairly brief apprenticeship ranged at this time from £2 to £4 a week.

Kilt-making for the army, a job described as "of national importance" also provided careers for several disabled men after training at Erskine and later in the factories of a Glasgow firm of military contractors. Bee-keeping classes, under an honorary bee-master, Mr Alec Steven, began at Erskine as early as 1916 and by the summer of 1917 more than 70 men were sufficiently skilled in this ancient pursuit to start up on their own account.

Instruction was also given in hairdressing, tailoring and French polishing. One graduate from the hairdressing class who found employment in a Glasgow salon wrote later: "The chaps who had an instructor like Jimmy Doig have a lot to be thankful for. He's one in a thousand".

Four years after the First World War Erskine-trained hairdressers, shoemakers, cabinet-makers and agriculturists were working at their trades in London and other parts of the United Kingdom, in Canada, Australia and even as far away as the Falkland Islands.

There were of course men so seriously disabled that they stood little chance of making their way on their own in the outside world and it was at Erskine that many of them found sanctuary; a permanent home with workshops facilities so accessible as to enable them to engage in rea-sonably congenial and, more important, financially rewarding employment.

In 1920 the workshops were extended to provide increased space for the expanding bootmaking, basketwork and cabinet-making depart-ments. Altogether at this time there were 10 different sections in what was now known as the Erskine Training Centre, employing a total of 140 trainees. By 1920, too, a total of 9,500 patients had been fitted with new limbs made in the workshops.

Throughout the years the workshops continued to be a focal point of the Erskine community, though, as repeatedly stressed in the Executive Committee's annual reports, at considerable financial cost. In October 1948, however, a major decision was taken on the workshops' future.

Following an expert study of the operation by the Glasgow industrialist Mr (later Sir Iain) Stewart, agreement was reached with the Ministry of Labour to incorporate the workshops under the Government's Sheltered Workshops scheme in place of the vocational training scheme which had operated since the end of World War I. Under this arrangement Erskine received a government grant towards the workshops wages bill and now became mainly a refuge for severely disabled men whose disabilities made them unlikely to find suitable employment in the competitive workaday world outside.

At the end of 1980 there were 41 full-time employees or trainees, 29 of whom were considered by the Employment Services Agency to be too badly disabled to work in other than sheltered conditions. They were employed in surgical bootmaking, upholstery and furniture repairs, French-polishing, printing, basketry and cane furniture making. There was also a six-acre market garden within the Erskine policies, which supplied the hospital kitchen with a plentiful supply of fresh produce.

Throughout the decades the hospital had a shop in various locations in Glasgow; in Sauchiehall Street, Wellington Street, and a brief appearance in West George Street, loaned by the Clydesdale Bank, before a move to King Street in 1989. The last named was closed in 1999 because of the competition from large stores and gift shops.

The shops originally sold items made in the workshops, but as patients got older and couldn't make things the way they did, because of arthritis and other debilitating conditions, products were bought from other manufacturers, which negated the purpose of the shop. In addition to the competition, money was being spent on the shops that could be more usefully spent on medical and nursing care.

There was also a shop in a tourist centre in Alexandria, Dunbartonshire, where craft items made at the hospital were sold; but this was also closed. The gift shop at the entrance to the hospital was closed in 2001 and incorporated into the garden centre.

Still going strong
after 50 years

In 1966 Erskine celebrated its 50th anniversary with a hard look at the future. There were still 11,000 war pensioners in Scotland from the 1914–18 war and 40,000 from 1939–45 and later wars. Only about half the disabled men at Erskine had disability pensions. During the following 10 years it was expected that the number of disabled men from the 1914–18 War would be greatly reduced but there would be a corresponding increase in applications for admissions to Erskine from ex-Servicemen of the 1939–45 War. Time proved this prediction to be only too accurate.

In 1966 Erskine's community of disabled ex-Servicemen included four veterans of the South African War, one aged 92 who had joined the Argylls in 1892 and was wounded on the Western Front in 1916. In Invernairn Ward there was a 75-year-old veteran who had lost a leg with the King's Own Scottish Borderers in the 1914–18 war; in 1965 his other leg had to be amputated, but such is the skill of Erskine's physiotherapists that he learned to walk on two artificial legs.

In the Harvie Anderson Ward, Roderick MacLeod (see page 85) who served with the Royal Corps of Signals during 1946–48 and was later paralysed by disseminated sclerosis, was showing great courage in attempting to cope with his affliction. And in the workshops at this time there was another veteran of the 1914–18 War, John Reid, who came to Erskine in 1924 to learn basket-making and was still working as foreman basket-maker. In its jubilee year Erskine was steadfastly fulfilling its primary task of caring for men who had served their country and who had suffered for it.

The 50th anniversary celebrations were marked by a civic reception in Glasgow's City Chambers where, in 1916, Sir William Macewen had launched the great venture. The Hospital's President, Lord Provost John Johnston, acted as host to a gathering which included patients, members of the Executive Committee, staff and representatives of organisations which had supported the hospital over the half-century of its existence.

On Sunday, October 2, a church service was held in the Mansion House gallery when some 30 of the original patients and staff were among a representative congregation. In his address, the Very Rev Dr Charles L Warr, Dean of the Chapel Royal in Scotland, looked back to the historic day when this great house, transformed into a hospital, threw open its doors not as an act of charity, but in fulfilment of a debt of honour.

It was a debt, said Dr Warr, owed by the nation to men who had suffered irreparable physical injury in defence of its liberty. It must be difficult for those who do not remember those now distant days to realise the magnitude of the problems that faced our country as the casualties of the First World War rapidly mounted to staggering proportions unprecedented in the history of armed conflict.

Half a century has passed and the role of Erskine Hospital had expanded to meet altered conditions and changing needs. It no longer cared only for the limbless but for all disabled ex-Servicemen – those disabled while on duty with the armed forces, and those who suffered disablement after leaving them.

Dr Warr said, *"Beneath this roof, and in the cottages that stand so picturesquely in the surrounding parklands, are disabled men who served our country, not only in the two great World Wars, but in every war in which, within living memory, it has been involved, from South Africa to Malaya and Korea. We have not come here this Sunday morning in order to issue an appeal for the maintenance of Erskine Hospital. We have come to offer our humble thanks to Almighty God for all that those who have served it have been enabled to do and to achieve during these past fifty years in the relief of pain and the restoration to fuller life of so many who, in the service of their country, suffered grievous impairment of their normal strength and activity. None-the-less it is well to remind ourselves that the invocation of the continued Divine blessing upon this place can only be made in sincerity, if it is accompanied by a dedicated determination on the part of those on whom its maintenance depends that they will never fail or falter in the fulfilment of their obligations towards it".*

Sir William Macewen and the men and women who rallied round him in 1916 would have said "amen" to that.

On September 25, 1979 Prince Charles paid his first visit to Erskine, arriving by helicopter from Balmoral. The highlight of a memorable day was the unveiling by the Prince of a plaque commemorating the gift of an X-ray unit, costing some £30,000, from the Army Benevolent Fund.

During an extensive and unhurried tour of the hospital the Prince stopped to chat with many of the patients, which of course is what royal walkabouts are all about. At the end of a visit notable for its informality it was announced that Prince Charles had been delighted to accept an invitation by the Executive Committee to become Erskine's Patron, the second royal patron in the hospital's history.

On July 7, 1981, only a few weeks before his wedding to Lady Diana Spencer, Prince Charles returned to Erskine where he delighted staff and patients alike by recalling the names and war service of some of the veterans he had met two years earlier. His main task that day was to formally open the Haig Ward, the latest addition to Erskine's expanding facilities and named after Field Marshal Earl Haig, British Commander-in-Chief in World War I.

And since the royal wedding was very much on everyone's mind Erskine decided to hand over its wedding present to the bridegroom himself, a pair of fireside log baskets made in the hospital workshops. It was a cheerful and relaxed occasion, which went out to the nation on television later that evening.

Everyone at the hospital who was able to do so joined the world at their television sets to see the wedding in St Paul's Cathedral on July 29, 1981. Residents and staff were saddened at the couple's divorce on August 28, 1996 and the Princess's cruel death in a car crash on August 31, 1997.

Throughout its 50 years there had been many royal visitors to Erskine but, oddly enough, until September 1967 the hospital had never been visited by a reigning Monarch. Some nine years earlier, in 1958, Prince Philip had toured the wards and chatted with many old sailors and soldiers, but on 20 September 1967 the Queen and Prince Philip stopped at Erskine Ferry en route to the launch of the new Cunarder, Queen Elizabeth II, at Clydebank. The Chairman, General Sir Gordon MacMillan of MacMillan, was there to welcome them and to present 12 of the patients and staff to the Queen.

The Executive Committee's report for 1967 said that over the years Morton Hall had been an invaluable asset as an indoor recreation centre while the wards were well-equipped with television and radio, but it was felt that there was a need for additional amenities. It was with considerable satisfaction therefore that the Executive Committee, thanks to a magnificent donation of £60,000 from the Trustees of the late Lady MacRobert, were able to go ahead with the building of a new Recreation Centre.

This facility, formally opened as the MacRobert Centre in 1968, comprised a canteen, games room and rest room where the patients could enjoy a chat with relatives and friends in pleasant surroundings and, more important, in privacy. From the late 1960s and into the 1970s the hospital's wards underwent a continuous process of upgrading. For Erskine was, and still is, more than a hospital; as the Commandant put it, "we cannot do enough to make the place look and feel like home".

Early in 1970, after months of anxiety and no little controversy, the monstrous shadow of a proposed industrial development, which would have posed an environmental and health hazard to Erskine Hospital and its inmates was finally lifted. This was the plan to build a £23 million oil refinery at Longhaugh Point, Bishopton, less than half a mile from the Erskine complex.

To propose to site such a project in close proximity to a hospital whose patients included World War I ex-Servicemen still suffering from the effects of gas warfare would seem, to most reasonable people, to be an act of monumental folly. Yet such was the power of the oil interests, backed by a jobs-at-any-price lobby that the issue hung in the balance until finally resolved by a statutory public enquiry.

This lasted eight weeks and cost Erskine some £3,000 in legal expenses. The hospital was represented by Mr G S Gimson, QC, who had been a prisoner-of-war with David Boyle in the Far East, and who marshalled the case against the proposed refinery with consummate skill. In March 1970 the Reporter, Sir Robert Russell, announced his findings: that the project be rejected, a decision upheld by the then Secretary of State Mr Willie (later Lord) Ross. Erskine could breathe again without fear of pollution.

For the Erskine community the highlight of 1971 was the visit of Princess Anne on the occasion of the opening of the new Erskine Bridge on July 2. The Princess landed in the hospital grounds by helicopter and spent some time meeting and talking with patients and staff. The opening of the toll bridge across the Clyde at Erskine undoubtedly made access to the hospital easier for staff and visitors but it also necessitated hospital vehicles making the crossing up to 30 times a day. However, as a result of representations made at a subsequent public enquiry into the bridge tolls, the Secretary of State granted facilities for five vehicles belonging to the hospital to cross free of charge on hospital business.

On October 17, 1976 Erskine celebrated its 60th anniversary, an historic occasion which brought together no fewer than 40 "old originals" from the 1914–18 War, including one sprightly veteran who motored all the way from Lincolnshire. An inter-denominational service of thanksgiving was conducted by the hospital padres, the Rev Douglas Alexander and the Rev James Murphy, and the Rev Dr William Morris of Glasgow Cathedral preached the sermon.

In the evening a reception for patients, staff and not least, the 1914–18 veterans, was attended by Viscount Muirshiel, Lord Lieutenant of Renfrewshire, and General MacMillan. Entertainment was provided by Scottish Opera's principal bass baritone, Bill McCue and the soprano Helen McArthur. Thirst-quenchers were generously and abundantly donated by the Distillers Company Ltd and in the words of Colonel Boyle it was a "fabulous party".

In 1977 Miss M A G Cameron, Matron since 1964, retired and was succeeded by Mrs Maureen E Lundie. In the same year the hospital was equipped with new boilers at a cost of £80,000, funded by the Mildred Thomson bequest (see page 95) and a year later the Mansion House was completely rewired.

In 1978 the death of the Resident Medical Officer, Dr James McCall, MC, was recorded with great regret by the Executive Committee. Dr McCall served the Erskine community faithfully and well for many years and his passing was keenly felt by both staff and patients. Dr McCall was succeeded by Dr Tom McFadyen. The death also occurred that year of Dr David Douglas, Consultant Physician, and a valued member of Erskine's skilled team. Dr Hugh Conway was appointed to succeed him.

Early in 1978 Erskine faced its bleakest financial crisis. The stark facts were unfolded by General MacMillan at the annual meeting of the Executive Committee on March 9; the hospital was now costing £1 million a year to run; inflation and a steep rise in oil costs had increased the annual fuel bill from £43,000 to £59,000; nurses' wages had gone up from £245,000 to £445,000 a year; and to make ends meet Erskine was dipping into capital, disposing of some of its investments and borrowing from the bank. The outlook at that time could truthfully be described as gloomy.

But Erskine had weathered similar economic lows before and while approaches were being made to both central and local government for increased support, Sir Gordon announced plans for an "Effort for Erskine" fund-raising scheme. One advertisement in particular helped to capture public attention: a cartoon, headed "Why Gordon needs your Help", personalised the plight of Erskine's disabled veterans.

It told in graphic terms the story of how Gordon Bucher, 52, a victim of tuberculosis resulting from his war service with the Royal Navy, had found sanctuary at Erskine. Public response to the "Effort for Erskine", to quote Sir Gordon, was "quite incredible".

Over the years the Scottish Office had also shown a sympathetic awareness of Erskine's problems and its claims to be considered as a special case. The difficulty, however, was to persuade Whitehall that these were both cogent and urgent. At this time Erskine was fortunate in having on its Executive Committee the Rt. Hon. Betty Harvie Anderson (later Baroness Skrimshire of Quarter) then Deputy Speaker of the House of Commons and daughter of the late Colonel Harvie Anderson, one of the hospital's founders.

At a meeting in the House of Commons, Betty Harvie Anderson, accompanied by Colonel Boyle, pleaded Erskine's case to Mr Alf Morris, Minister Responsible for War Pensions. Mr Morris had already been comprehensively briefed on the hospital's plight by Mr Harry Ewing, MP, Scottish Under Secretary with responsibility for health matters, but there is no doubt that Betty Harvie Anderson's eloquent espousal of Erskine's cause was an important factor in influencing the Minister's subsequent decision to come to the hospital's aid.

In June, Mr Ewing announced that the government was to bear the cost of every war pensioner undergoing treatment for his pensionable disability and was prepared to accept responsibility for the support of some 30 additional ex-Service patients who would otherwise be in NHS hospitals. This welcome arrangement had the effect of raising the level of government support towards pensioners and Health Board admissions from 14.5 per cent to 20 per cent of Erskine's total expenditure. It was appropriate that Mr Ewing should make the announcement during a visit to Erskine when he assured the Executive Committee that the Home and Health Department was well aware of the hospital's financial problems and promised a review of government aid from time to time.

The seriousness of the 1978 crisis is illustrated by the fact that during it Erskine had to use about £100,000 of its capital, which had been reduced to £800,000. The public, of course, as General MacMillan gratefully acknowledged, had once again rallied to the hospital's support with unparalleled generosity. In his report at the year's end Mr J A Young, Treasurer, also expressed his understandable satisfaction with a truly astonishing turnaround in the balance sheet:

"Last year when I recorded our thanks for the peak level of ordinary donations we had received, no one would have dared to forecast that the year which is now under review would show more than twice as much – but the £336,055 in the accounts is in fact fractionally more. Not only that, but the number of subscribers rose from 3,150 to 7,864 – again a peak figure. To all who have helped us beat our troubles, I express our deep gratitude and to our new benefactors a warm welcome…the whole nation seems to have rallied to our cause".

Homes for veterans

Princess Park in the Erskine Estate has 59 cottages that are reserved for war pensioners and their families. The first of the cottages were built for disabled men and their families in September 1946. The money came from the Glasgow and West of Scotland Branch of the Navy League War Comforts Fund. The money for another cottage was provided Miss Dot Allan in memory of her mother Mrs Jean Weir Luke Allan. These in turn were shortly added to by an additional 10 cottages erected by the Scottish Veterans Garden City Association

This post-war development was one of the most important in Erskine's history for it enabled disabled men employed in the workshops not only to live near their place of work but close to the hospital facilities on which so many of the war veterans depended. As Major Gilbert Rankin, former Secretary and Treasurer, recalled, "It had a further significant effect in that the committee, in addition to its concern for the disabled men themselves, felt it also had to consider the welfare of the families who had now set up their home within the Erskine enclave and for whom social and other amenities (a small Community Centre was one) were necessary".

The Housing Estate continued to expand in the post-war years. The Executive Committee, in co-operation with Renfrew County Council, formed the Erskine Hospital Housing Society and erected a further 10 houses. Subsequently another 29 grant-aided houses went up bringing the total built by the Housing Society to 39. These, the Executive Committee decided, in a new and practical demonstration of Erskine's concern for those in its care, should be occupied by disabled ex-Servicemen and their families free of rent and rates.

In 1979 the 10 cottages owned by the Scottish Veterans Garden City Association were generously made over to the hospital and integrated into its facilities. "This means we now have 50 cottages available to disabled ex-servicemen and their families," General Sir Gordon

MacMillan noted in his report for that year. "They live a full family life, free of rent and rates but know that they have the full support of the hospital should they need it".

The 1991 report also announced that with the advent of gas within the estate some 75% of the cottages were being converted from solid fuel to gas with all the attendant advantages of a cleaner, more efficient and controllable source of heating. Smoke alarms had also been fitted.

The cost of maintaining the cottages rose steeply over the years, and in 2000 upkeep was running at £80,000 a year and discussions were held with the tenants on the feasibility of charging a rent which would help to generate more income for the hospital and help it to pay for its many commitments. The idea did not meet any opposition from the tenants when it was emphasised that no-one would be disadvantaged by any new policy.

Among a number of options was one which suggested that cottages could be refurbished as they became vacant and might be re-let at an economic rent to either new tenants or current tenants who were prepared to move into the refurbished property on the approved terms. The new conditions would include security of tenure through the new single social tenancy and access to housing benefit, depending on the financial position of individual tenants.

A 20-year search for a suitable holiday home for patients from Erskine Hospital at Bishopton ended in 1993 when Erskine House was opened in Dunoon, Argyll. Vice-Admiral Sir Thomas Baird, Erskine's Chairman, commented, "Most of our patients are long-term and have never been away from the place for more than a day's outing. Some of them have not been far from the hospital for as long as 20 years.

While the facilities at Erskine are being constantly improved patients, like the rest of us, still need a change of scenery, food, routine and a whiff of sea air from time to time".

Erskine House in Dunoon is a detached converted villa at 147 Alexandra Parade. It has accommodation for eight residents who can spend up to three weeks there. During their holiday many entertainment events are provided, including runs in the Home's own minibus, which is adapted for wheelchairs. There is also a guest room where a relative can stay during the holiday.

As in any other Erskine facility, there is a higher ratio of nurses to holiday-makers in order that 24-hour nursing care may be provided. The manager is Sister Jean Ward who succeeded Mrs Pat Constable in March 2000.

The villa, bought for £130,000 and converted at a cost of £900,000, is close to the shoreline with magnificent, uninterrupted views to the east and south over the Firth of Clyde. Access to the town centre, 10 minutes walk away, is easy by wheelchair. A major consideration in the choice of site was that it should be no farther than 400 yards from a pub, betting shop and post office.

"It was an expensive operation but I know that no-one would grudge the men and women of Erskine who had given so much in the service of their country", said Vice-Admiral Sir Thomas Baird. By the spring of 2001 more than 1000 places had been taken at Dunoon, some by residents who had been there several times.

The search for a suitable building for the Holiday Home and its purchase and rebuilding were all supervised by a small sub-committee under the chairmanship of Mr Bill McNeil, a member of the Executive Committee. Bill served in the Royal Corps of Signals for six years from 1939 and later became Director of Social Work for Renfrewshire, and Depute Director of Social Work for Strathclyde Regional Council when that body was set up in 1974.

He joined Erskine's Executive Committee in 1978 and was a frequent visitor to the Dunoon Home until his death in October 2000 at the age of 84. He was succeeded as chairman of the Dunoon Committee by Mrs Netta Macpherson.

The remarkable
Roddy McLeod

R oddy McLeod served in the Royal Corps of Signals as a National
Serviceman in the late 1940s. In 1950 he graduated bachelor of
science at Glasgow University and was teaching physics at Johnstone
High School, Renfrewshire, when he was struck down by multiple
sclerosis.

He came to Erskine in 1965 and three years later, gained a degree in
mathematics from the Open University. That was enough to get him
nationwide headlines because Roddy was paralysed from the neck
down. Nine years later, he astonished the country again when he gained
an honours degree. Among his subjects were complex analysis, number
theory and logic, graph theory and design and numerical computation,
subjects that are difficult enough for a healthy person.

Mr George Arkieson, Scottish Director of the University at the time,
said: "This is an incredible achievement for someone with such disability.
I doubt if this feat has been equalled since the University started teaching
in 1971". Mr Arkieson added that Roddy's success highlighted the value
of a hospital like Erskine, where long-term patients were given constant
individual attention, medical and nursing care, and the mechanical aids to
enable them to do things they could not do in any other hospital.

Because of his paralysis, all Roddy's reading was done with the help of
automatic page turners; books were supported on a plastic and metal
frame. The written work for his degree was done with a computerised
typewriter, the keys of which were activated by a highly complex series
of sucks and blows into a tube in Mr McLeod's mouth. The typewriter
did not have all the mathematical symbols involved in Roddy's studies so
he did many of the calculations mentally. Two other smaller tubes into
which Mr McLeod blew controlled the guidance system for his
wheelchair.

Roddy died at the age of 77 in 1999 after 34 years at Erskine. His
stay there was the second longest since it opened in 1916[1]. To every

interviewer, and there were many, he readily acknowledged that without the care he received at Erskine he could never have done the things he did.

Another paralysed patient, Dan Samson, used a mouth-controlled computerised typewriter to write an 80,000-word romantic novel based on the Roman invasion of Britain. If you wonder what it's like to be paralysed, think how you would scratch your nose when it's itchy.

George Collins was a 19-year-old corporal when a 500lb IRA landmine blew up his armoured car near Omagh and killed three of his comrades. George lay unconscious and paralysed from brain, chest, arm and leg injuries in various hospitals for months before he regained consciousness. It took many months for him to come out of danger but he still couldn't speak, walk, read or write.

Then he was admitted to Erskine Hospital in 1972 and a long period of nursing and rehabilitation followed before he could do all the things he couldn't do before then. In the early days he was told,

"Go and play bowls".

"How can I play bowls?", he sobbed, "my hands don't work. I'm on sticks".

"Oh well if you're going to let a little thing like that…"

So George got down on his knees, clutched a wood in two numbed hands and played bowls. Now George lives with his wife Joy and two children Lynsey and Amanda in a cottage in the hospital grounds. "Erskine gave me back my life", he says. "It's as simple as that".

The late Sam Newell, who retired in 1977 after 40 years as a physiotherapist at the hospital, spoke of the "spirit of Erskine" although that mysterious quality is not easy to define and certainly is not paraded for inspection. Sam Newell came to Erskine from Glasgow's Royal Infirmary in 1937, served as a Sergeant in the Royal Army Medical Corps from 1941 to 1945 with the 13th General Hospital in the Middle East, and had seen Erskine in many of its progressive developments.

Several thousand disabled men passed through his skilled hands and if anyone could testify to the spirit of Erskine he could. He spoke of one man in particular whose fortitude in the face of his appalling disability will long be remembered by everyone fortunate to have known him.

Jack Easson was blown up in the Battle of Loos in 1917. When he came to in a shell-hole and discovered that what was left of his left arm was useless, he tried to pull the trigger on himself with his right hand, only to find that that was shattered too. After being in hospital in Epsom for some time, with his left arm obviously gone and a huge bandage wrapped round his right arm, they told him they had amputated the right as well.

So here was a man who eventually wore two artificial arms, who taught himself to write a beautiful copperplate, could use a typewriter, wash and shave himself, took himself home from Erskine across country to Callander every week-end, was a first-class billiards player and won all the sprint championships at the Erskine sports.

Jack Easson, after undergoing training in office and commercial work at Erskine, became manager of the hospital workshops, which he ran with exemplary efficiency until retirement in 1965. He died in 1968. "No one could meet a finer, cheerier man, a man who got on with his job and did it well under a tremendous handicap", said Sam Newell. "Jack Easson was a shining example of what the spirit of Erskine is all about".

David Boyle, one-time Commandant of Erskine, told the story of the survivor of the 1916 Battle of the Somme who used to talk to his artificial leg, especially after he'd had one or two beers or wee whiskies more than he could carry. He used to take off his peg leg after he'd made it back to the hospital and lay it beside his bedside.

"If you don't bloody well behave yersel' in future", he'd say, "I'll throw you oot the bloody window and let you fend for yersel'".

John Reid came to Erskine in November 1917. In August of that year, while serving with the 18th Battalion, Highland Light Infantry, he took part in a bombing raid to "straighten up the line". He had just gone over the top when shell exploded near him. When he woke up in a field hospital the man in the bed next to him said, "Hello, mate, how did you cop it?"

"I told him how I'd been hit but I really didn't know how bad", said John, and the bloke in the next bed said, 'I've lost a leg' and when I sympathised with him he answered, 'Don't feel sorry for me, mate; start feeling sorry for yourself, you've lost a leg too.'"

In the Luftwaffe blitz on Clydeside in 1941 several incendiary bombs landed on Erskine's roof when John Reid was on fire watch. "I just happened to be on the roof when they fell so I kicked them off and broke a bone in my good foot", he said.

Paratrooper Donald Kelly jumped with the 6th Airborne Division at the Battle of Arnhem in 1944 and was so severely wounded in the epic fight for Arnhem Bridge that both his legs had to be amputated. At Erskine he was fitted with two artificial limbs on which he began the slow and painful process of learning to walk again. In time Donald Kelly became as mobile as a man on two artificial legs ever is, so mobile in fact that getting down to the Golf Inn at Bishopton for a night out was no problem.

It was getting back that was Donald's trouble. His method of entry, once he had negotiated the journey back to Erskine after closing time, was to open a ground-floor window, throw both his legs in first and then hoist himself in after them. Donald Kelly was determined not to dwell on what he could not do on two artificial limbs but rather on what he could do, and with the support and encouragement of Erskine's staff and his mates he succeeded in accomplishing a great deal.

In 1961 Donald went to Wembley on the disastrous day when England beat Scotland 9-3. By the time the ninth goal had eluded the unfortunate Scottish goalkeeper Frank Haffey, Donald had knocked back most of the half-bottle of the good stuff he had taken to the game with him. As the subdued Scottish fans made their way towards the exits after the final whistle a London bobby watched Donald weaving erratically from one crush barrier to the next.

"Cor stone the crows", said the copper, "that geezer's stoned as a newt!"

"Aye, and he's got no legs either", one of Donald's pals told the copper.

Donald Kelly first came to Erskine in 1946 and during his period of rehabilitation he met and married one of the nurses and was subsequently allocated one of the cottages within the hospital grounds. After training he was appointed canteen manager and later supervised the MacRobert Memorial Centre, which catered for all the disabled men, staff and visitors. In the years during which he held these posts his unfailing cheerfulness, sharp wit and extraordinary mobility became well known in the Erskine community. He died in 1974 aged 55.

Bill Sneddon lost both legs in September 1918, fighting with the Highland Light Infantry in the Ypres Salient. He lay in the open for two days and three nights before being picked up and taken to the Casualty Clearing Station at Poperinghe. He reached Erskine in 1919 via Stobhill Military Hospital and Bangour Hospital, West Lothian.

At Erskine he began the slow, painful and humiliating process of learning to walk on two provisional legs. "I got about reasonably well", he recalled. "I had two peg legs at the time and I used to totter up and down with the help of two sticks in a place called the Gallery. I made good progress and was discharged on 21 June 1919".

As a boy in Selkirk Bill Sneddon had played golf, so, as he said, " I had a bash until I gave up the game in the thirties". But it was at bowls that he demonstrated a skill astonishing in a man with two artificial legs How on earth did he manage, with his handicap, to cope with the problem of delivering a bowl? "I didn't attempt to get down to it", he explained, "but

I could bend a wee bit…". Bill went on to win his place in a Civil Service rink that triumphed in an international championship in 1935.

Until his death, aged 79, Bill Sneddon had been in and out of Erskine since 1919. Like most men who had lost a leg or legs, he suffered from "phantom feet", which, as the term implies, means an acute awareness of feet and especially of toes that are not there. "The awful thing about it is that it keeps you from sleeping, for you can still feel your toes as if they were actually there". Bill Sneddon lived with life on two artificial legs, and help from Erskine, for 60 years.

Bill McDowall, a former Scots Guardsman who fought in the Falklands, didn't lose a limb. He walks with a stick, but it was with the mental scars of war Bill found most difficulty in coping. He came to Erskine in 1997 after his discharge on medical grounds.

"Until I came to Erskine, no-one really took seriously the trauma I was going through", he says. Bill now lives in one of the veterans' cottages with his wife Beverley and their four children. He is the Information Technology Manager and is kept busy working on the hospital's website, another example of Erskine moving with the times. "I really enjoy living and working here. Erskine has certainly changed my life for the better".

John (Skin) Cunningham came out of the army in 1939 after about 12 years' service. By the time he reached Erskine Hospital he had a serious drink problem, although he didn't consider it a problem. He just walloped it down. He was never seen without the ivory-handled walking stick he bought in the hospital craft shop. Skin got his nickname from playing in an Army band, presumably on the drums. He tended to express himself with some vehemence verbally and physically.

Two footpads once tried to mug him in Anderston Bus Station and Skin beat them up with his stick, a feat that earned him considerable column inches in the Glasgow newspapers as a courageous war hero.

One day he met Colonel Steele in a hospital corridor after a session with a doctor. "The stupid b… said I had only three months to live and told me to give up smokin'", said Skin. "Whit the hell's the point in that?" he asked indignantly. Almost three months to the day later Skin was dead.

Joe Henry is in his 80s and will never be able to erase the terrible memories of the severe beatings he suffered in a Japanese prisoner of war camp during World War II. For three-and-a half years the Royal Army Service Corps man was beaten if he failed to lower his eyes passing a guard, or if he collapsed from exhaustion in the mines. The physical scars all but healed but the mental scars did not. Joe has been looked after at Erskine for 45 years. He and his wife Mary lived in one of the veterans' cottages until Mary died in March 2001.

"Time is a great healer", says Joe, "but the best healer of all has been Erskine – it has been our life". One person whose visits he looks forward to is from his son Hugh, who was brought up in Erskine. He is now a member of the Scottish Parliament.

One day as I was leaving the hospital I met Philip McKenna, a war-time prisoner of war in Poland for five years. He was wearing a badge on his lapel proclaiming he had been at Erskine 36 years. When I asked him about the hospital he said, "It should be named Erskine Haven. There's not another place like it".

"Call me Duke", he added.

"Why Duke?"

"Cos my name's Philip!", he said with a chuckle.

Mr McKenna never mentioned his years as a prisoner of war in our conversation. Nor did he give me any tips from that day's horse racing programme. Phil was an avid reader of racing pages and handed out tips liberally to anyone who would listen. His record of successes was not impressive. In November 1996, Erskine's 80th anniversary year, he went to London to attend the Festival of Remembrance in the Albert Hall. Another patient, Dr David Anderson, who assisted the Chief Surgeon at Erskine in 1940 as a final year medical student, went with him. They were accompanied by Staff Nurse Theresa Holland and nursing auxiliary Robert Dobelis. Mr McKenna died in June 2000 at the age of 80.

---

[1]One of the shortest stays in Erskine was, sadly, that of Mr James Sweeny, a Gordon Highlander from 1944 to 1948, who was admitted on June 25, 2001 and died only seven days later. Mr Sweeney was the father of Mrs Maureen Mosson, wife of Mr Alex Mosson, Lord Provost of Glasgow.

The things people
do for Erskine

People do the most astonishing things to raise money for Erskine. They jump, climb, deep sea dive, hold raffles, push beds, diet, lay bricks, organise car boot sales, hold exhibitions, play golf, walk backwards, run, cycle, sell things, buy things, cook, rattle cans, organise concerts and fetes and drink gallons of coffee. Sometimes the result of their labours is a few pounds, and at other times many thousands. All of it is gratefully received.

Six businessmen from Paisley climbed the glaciers and the five peaks of the Ötztal Alps in Austria at altitudes of more than 9,000 feet to raise money for the hospital. Mark Pender, whose uncle is a resident in Erskine, washed cars and wheelie bins. A group from The Parachute Regiment climbed all 284 of Scotland's Munros, peaks of 3,000ft or more.

Volunteer staff members of Erskine pushed 12 wheelchair-bound residents 20 miles to Renfrew, Paisley and back to Bishopton to help pay for a minibus. Television sports commentator Arthur Montford helped to raise £18,000 for a new bus. Local policemen cycled to the scene of the 1944 Normandy Landings in France and so impressed the local Mayor in Caen with their effort he gave them a civic reception.

In 1985 seven-year-old Craig Porter met his great grandfather, 91-year-old Mr Bill McCabe, for the first time when he went to Erskine with other pupils of Gavinburn Primary School, Old Kilpatrick, to present a cheque for £411 they had raised. Understandably there were a few happy tears shed.

In 1987 a former Royal Air Force clerk did a parachute jump for the first time – at the age of 79. In 1993 Parcelforce staff in Glasgow gave the hospital a £500 cheque they won for being the best sorting centre in the country.

Charlie Baird, a former Scots Guardsman and SAS man who lived in a war veteran's cottage, collected foreign coins handed over by toll-dodging motorists on the Erskine Bridge – lire, drachmas, francs and pesetas – and a friendly bank converted them into pounds.

George Ross, Legion Affairs Officer with the Royal British Legion Scotland, Private Ricky Foster, King's Own Scottish Borderers and Petty Officer Kevin Cave of the Royal Navy spent three weeks on a 1,999-mile cycle trip around Scotland, finishing up by cycling along the corridors of the hospital and into the games room to cheers from staff and residents. Their efforts raised £30,000.

In February 1986 Craig Caldwell, a 26-year-old sports agent from Milngavie, completed his lone round of all 499 Scottish peaks over 2,500ft with a pre-dawn start from a Lomondside Youth Hostel to the top of Ben Lomond.

Closing the charity epic that had kept him away from home for exactly 377 days, he jubilantly hoisted himself on to the summit triangulation pillar and said, "Thank goodness that's the last of these blighters for a while".

Mr Caldwell gave up his business for the climbs, which cost him £4,000. He slept mainly in tents and mountain bothies and for transport used only his legs and a pushbike. He walked 3,000 miles, cycled 2,500 miles and climbed more than 150,000 feet in a single journey. His climbs included all 284 Munros and all 220 Corbetts (peaks between 2,500ft and 3,000ft). His efforts raised £16,000 for Erskine.

All Munros and Corbetts have been climbed many times but never before on a single trip. Hamish Brown first completed all the Munros in one trek of 112 days in 1974.

Mr Martin Moran, who bagged all the Munros in a single tour in the winter of 1984–85, called Mr Caldwell's achievement "the most remarkable British mountain walk of all".

In 1994 a group of Star Trek enthusiasts showed some episodes of the cult television series in the Tudor Hotel in Airdrie at £5 a time for adults and £3 for children, and raised several hundred pounds. Glasgow police raised £4,000 by selling 10,000 enamel lapel badges depicting Rikki Fulton as the cheeky Supercop in BBC television's *Scotch and Wry*. The sale of Model-T Ford vans, at £16 each, carrying the emblem of Strathclyde Police, brought in £2000.

On a Sunday evening in October 1996 an all-star concert in Paisley Town Hall in aid of hospital funds featured Jimmy Logan, Johnnie Beattie, Andy Cameron, Peggy O'Keefe, the Lowland Band of the Scottish Division and the Tara Irish Dance Team, all of whom gave their services free.

In May 1999 Major Garry McLeod of Tayforth University Officer Training Corps in Stirling walked backwards 50 miles to Erskine to raise money for the hospital. Stirling University staff gave him a pasta breakfast to fortify him for the walk. The 43-year-old major already held the Scottish record for walking backwards.

He said that when he was a boy in Wick, which is close to John O'Groats, "We used to see people doing all sorts of bizarre things, either starting or finishing there".

Cathie MacDonald gave Erskine the £5,500 cheque she won playing Celebrity Wheel of Fortune. Glasgow Airport fire-fighters raised money for Erskine by walking 35 miles a day for four days in Holland.

A swimming event organised by the Royal Bank of Scotland Swimming Club in The Royal Commonwealth Pool in February 2001, in which 350 swimmers took part, raised more than £17,000 for Edinburgh Erskine.

Andrew Robertson, Secretary of the hospital, is an enthusiastic climber, to put it mildly. His climbing in various parts of the world has benefited several charities. On one occasion he left his city centre office and books on the Scottish Principles of Private Law and the Law of Delict to climb the 22,800-feet high Aconcagua in Argentina, the highest mountain in the Western Hemisphere.

To get there he flew 7,000 miles from Glasgow to London to Madrid to Buenos Aires and then another 600 miles across Argentina to Mendoza on the West coast.

From the road-head at Puenta del Inca he walked for two days to the base camp at Plaza de Mulas and a rise in altitude from 2,700 metres to 4,200 metres. "This has a noticeable effect on one", said Mr Andy Bloom of OTT Expeditions, who accompanied him. "It's no push-over", said Mr Bloom. "Although it's a very popular climb many people who attempt the mountain go home disappointed".

And Mr Robertson commented characteristically, "It's not all such hard going. On the way back there is a whole day in Mendoza, the wine producing centre of Argentina, and a tour of the huge Penaflores winery, the second largest commercial winery in the world. And the weather is warm, too!".

Aconcagua is close to the border with Chile. Parts of the range are very exposed and in a storm are subject to the full force of the winds, which roar across the mountain and can destroy a camp in minutes. That particular adventure benefited Erskine to the tune of £5,000.

Andrew has climbed the Alps in Europe, the Rockies in North

America and the Blue Mountain in Jamaica. His wife Sheila commented, "Some husbands play golf, some play squash, some collect match box covers and mine climbs mountains! It takes all kinds".

Andrew's mother's cousin, Muriel Cuthbert, married a resident, Tom Hagan, while working as a war-time occupational therapist in Erskine. His father Alec was in the Territorial Army from the 1920s to the early 50s, ending as Brevet-Colonel in command of 591 Mixed Anti-Aircraft/Searchlights RA, Cameronians TA until 1954, and his uncle Vice-Admiral Sir John Cuthbert commanded, at different times, HMS Glasgow and HMS Ajax and helped to plan D-Day in 1944. Sir John's wife Betty, now in her 97th year, set up the Women's Fire Brigade in London during the war-time blitz in 1940.

Andrew is Senior Partner of the Glasgow legal firm of T C Young & Son, and has been Secretary of Erskine Hospital since 1976, making him the hospital's second longest-serving Secretary. His knowledge of Erskine is encyclopaedic and the matters of employment law, contracts, compensation and every other legal issue he has handled on the hospital's behalf are impossible to compute.

Although his post is a paid one, he gives the charitable aspect of Erskine as much time and attention as he does to the other charities, such as The Princess Royal Trust for Carers, in which he is involved. Andrew has been Secretary and Legal Advisor to the Trust since 1990. He has been a member of Greater Glasgow Health Board since 1999 and has chaired a number of National Health Service Trusts including the Greater Glasgow Primary Care NHS Trust. He was appointed OBE in 1994 for his work in helping to set up community-based housing associations throughout Glasgow.

This catalogue of efforts for Erskine could go on for ever, but very occasionally the darker side of man's nature manifests itself. In 1989 someone stole a casket containing the charter presented to Erskine by the hospital's patron Princess Louise. What possible profit that brought to the thief is difficult to imagine. And in the same year someone stole a gallon bottle of coins to the value of £300 from the Army Careers Office in Queen Street, Glasgow. It really does take all kinds to make our imperfect world.

Mildred and John

One of the most touching stories connected with Erskine, described by the *Daily Telegraph* as "a poignant and enduring love story" and *The Ayrshire Post* as "one of the great love stories of the century" concerned someone who had never even visited the hospital.

On Friday, November 4, 1977, a ward was ceremonially named The Lauder-Thomson Ward in memory of Captain John Lauder, who was killed in France by an exploding shell on December 28, 1916. The Captain was the only son of the famous Scots comedian, Sir Harry Lauder.

For six decades from that day, a lady named Mildred Thomson cherished the memory of the 22-year-old Argyll and Sutherland Highlander to whom she was engaged for only a few months. And when she died in London in 1975 at the age of 83, still unmarried, she left £80,000, the residue of her sizeable estate, to Erskine Hospital to provide "some amenity for the hospital in memory of my late fiancé".

The hospital boilers were then 61 years old and clapped-out. David Boyle, the Commandant, commented, "We used Mildred's legacy to buy new boilers, which served the admirable purpose of keeping our veterans warm, and later we named a ward after her and Captain Lauder. After all", said Colonel Boyle with a smile, "We could hardly call them the Lauder-Thomson boilers!".

Mildred Thomson lived in London most of her life. She came to know of Erskine Hospital through Sir Harry, who had visited the hospital many times, and who constantly praised it for the work it was doing to rehabilitate injured and ailing Servicemen. Although she promised to go to Erskine with Sir Harry one day, she never did but she never forgot the things Sir Harry had told her about it.

The love story of John Lauder and Mildred Thomson began, though they did not know it, when they were children. They met when she lived with her parents in Wishaw, Lanarkshire, and John with his parents a few miles away in Hamilton. When Mildred's father retired from farming, the family went to live in Peckham, London. Later, the Lauders bought a house in Tooting, also in London, and the two young people met again. In the late summer of 1916 they became engaged while John was in the Army. The two families were delighted.

A few months later, on January 1, 1917, on the dawn of what was to have been a joyful year for all of them, Harry Lauder was appearing in a highly successful review, "Three Cheers", at the Shaftesbury Theatre, London, when a telegram containing only two words was handed to him at his hotel. It came from his wife in Scotland and it said, "John killed".

Harry Lauder was numb with grief. A steady stream of London society came to his hotel to offer him their sympathy, but the man who had made millions laugh all over the world was unable to see any of them, with one exception, the girl who was to have been his daughter-in-law. She stayed with Harry for several days intercepting the many telegrams and letters of condolence delivered to the hotel.

Among the sympathisers were Queen Alexandra, widow of Edward VII, Prime Minister Lloyd George, the Earl of Derby, George Robey, Vesta Tilley, Sir Thomas Dewar, Sir Thomas Lipton and others from every class of society.

Only hours after being given the tragic news, Mildred had received John's last letter from France. She never recovered from her grief. For 58 years she kept a leather-bound scrapbook containing 280 newspaper cuttings about John's death.

Once when Harry was in pantomime in Manchester he was so anxious to see his son that after a Saturday night show he caught the midnight train north, arrived at Gourock at 5 a.m. on Sunday, and as there was no steamer or motor boat, he paid two fishermen to take him the five miles across the Firth of Clyde.

The weather was so rough they had to turn back, but the anxious father was persistent, and persuaded the two fishermen to try again a little later. After a three-hour struggle in heavy seas the three men reached Dunoon numbed by cold and sodden clothing,

When Harry Lauder was knighted in 1919 for his work for the troops and the Allied cause, his wife said: "How my boy would have rejoiced at this Royal recognition of his father's worth and work".

Lady Lauder died in 1927, and her husband in 1950 at the age of 80, but the story of his love for his son and Mildred Thomson's undying devotion to his memory live on.

The Mansion House.

Erskine Home in the 21st century.

Above: James Aitken, former Cameron Highlander, was one of the last veterans of the First World War to be cared for at Erskine. He died in 1997, aged 101 years.

Right: Colonel Martin Gibson, who served with The Royal Scots, with members of his Regimental Recruiting Team and pupils from Edinburgh schools, who helped raise money for the hospital by completing an Army assault course.

Matron Maureen Lundie (now retired) with Mr James Piggot,
a former Royal Military Policeman.

Staff members Isobel Duffy, Cindy Murray, Christine Winters and
Gordon MacPherson dressed up for a fund-raising event.

Prince Charles has a word with Mrs Mollie Craig, one of Erskine's enthusiastic fund-raisers.

The Duke of Kent meets former spitfire pilot Robert Kirkwood.

The Princess Royal formally opens Erskine Mains watched by Mrs Lorraine Ross, Director of Nursing and Tom McFadyen, Director of Medical Services.

An evening's entertainment with Jimmy Logan.

*George Manners meets Prince Charles. "Do you sleep with that leg on?"
asked the Prince.*

Resident Gladys Clark, ex-Royal Navy, with Cheryl O'Neill, an Occupational Therapy Assistant.

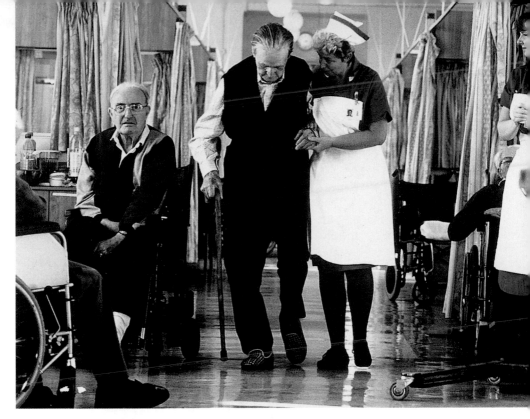

One of the wards that was in use until the move to Erskine Home.

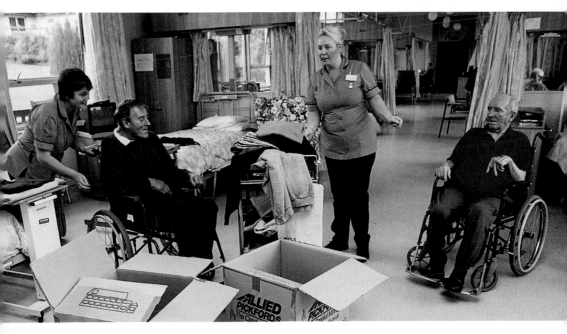

Preparing for the move to the new Erskine Home.

Top: *A game of dominoes in the Activities Room.*

Middle: *The café in Erskine Home is open to residents staff and visitors.*

Bottom: *Mr Iain Grimmond, Director of Finance (left) and Colonel Booby Steele, Director of Support Services, in the Reception at Erskine Home.*

Bill MacLauchlan (second from the right) a former RAMC sergeant celebrates his 82nd birthday with some fellow residents.

Morning in busy Physiotherapy. Mr Hector Gangel, Erskine Home's oldest resident at 97 and a former Royal Scots Fusilier, gets a helping hand from Mrs Kate Lowe, Senior Physiotherapist.

Ms Jean Stewart, a former NAAFI girl (above) and Ronnie Lindsay, a former Pay Corps man, look out to the garden from their rooms in Erskine Mains.

The entrance to Erskine Mains Home.

The Garden Centre.

Keith Taylor, Director of Workshops and Trading (left) and a colleague discuss some Erskine Pine products. (Inset) Mr William McGeechan at work in the modern, well-equipped Erskine Pine Factory.

Some of the wide variety of items produced at Erskine Print.

Erskine offers help in the Gulf War

As evidence of the continuous process of improving facilities in the hospital, the Chairman's Report for 1988 said that, with the increasing frailty and age of patients, the number of nursing aids, particularly lifting equipment, had been substantially improved throughout the hospital.

"The support services have had a busy year with major staff changes within the Social Work and Speech Therapy departments. These have been achieved smoothly and the services they provide have been much appreciated by patients and their relatives. The dental, chiropody and optician services continue to provide essential back-up to the medical and nursing staff".

"There are plans to increase the scope and range of the Occupational Therapy department including the use of computing equipment within the coming year. The Physiotherapy department, in its refurbished premises, has been as busy as ever and the roof improvements carried out at the latter end of the year will, hopefully, eliminate the damp problems experienced during the last few years".

Admiral Baird also reported that the new Invernairn Ward extension had come into service and was proving a most welcome and much needed improvement to that ward, particularly in the dining and sitting-out arrangements, which were now much more comfortable and domestic in character. "I am very grateful to all those generous people who subscribed to its building costs, and in particular to the Queen Mary's Roehampton Hospital Trust which contributed a handsome £50,000 towards our costs".

In 1988, too, Dr Joan McAlpine, a Consultant in the Royal Alexandra Hospital in Paisley, was welcomed on to the Executive Committee as a Consultant Geriatrician with wide experience in caring for elderly and long-term patients. Dr McAlpine became chairman of the Medical Committee, later renamed the Health Care Committee, on which she has suggested many improvements in the care and conditions of patients. Her expertise was frequently displayed in the years-long deliberations on the shape and form of the new Erskine. It was while working with Dr McAlpine in the RAH that Dr Tom McFadyen gained his geriatric experience.

As the Annual Report for 1990 went to press the chairman reported, "The conflict in the Gulf is a cause for major national concern and in particular the war casualties that may result. The hospital has offered its services to the Ministry of Defence and this has been gratefully received. Contingency planning is in hand and we expect to make available some 25 bed-spaces immediately, and within the next few months a further 75 when the new wing is finished".

"This will put a very considerable strain on all our resources, but I am confident that Erskine will rise to this challenge to help the present generation of Servicemen and women as it did, and has done over the past 75 years".

As it happened the hospital did not receive any casualties from the Gulf War, but the war did cause some anxiety in my own family. My younger son Michael, a lawyer, was working at the time for the Israel Attorney General in the town of Dimona deep in the Negev desert of Israel.

Some time later I wrote, "Bad nights when I can't sleep are all too frequent, but one of them was worse than most. It was the night in January 1991 when Saddam Hussein attacked Israel with Scud missiles, some of which landed near Dimona. I lay awake all night listening to radio reports of the attack and praying that my son and his wife would not come to any harm".

In 1991 the canteen was significantly upgraded with new catering and back-of-counter facilities and new lavatories were provided. The opportunity was taken in the late summer, using Pearson Ward as a decanting ward, to redecorate five other wards. With the ever-increasing number of cars coming into the grounds the creation of a new park adjacent to the new workshops had helped to alleviate (but not solve!) the car-parking problem, particularly at weekends. Substantial fabric and roof repairs were carried out on the Mansion House.

Grateful as Erskine has been for the use of the Mansion House for more than 80 years, it sometimes gave the Executive Committee a severe shock in the extent of dry rot, deterioration of windows, roof and stonework, which necessitated a major programme of repairs, made possible by the financial support of its many benefactors.

The nurses of Erskine

Britain's nurses are rarely out of the news. In 2000 they made headlines when a poll by Market and Opinion Research International (MORI) for the Royal College of Nursing revealed that they felt the need to attract more people into nursing was even more important than more pay, although one must not infer that financial reward for their work is not an important consideration. Many were frustrated because there were not enough of them to enable them to give patients the attention they needed, a point that is repeatedly made by their representative organisations.

It is this desire to care that motivates the nurses of Erskine. Nursing care and therapy have always played a crucial part in the daily routine of Erskine, but equally important is the emphasis on long-term rehabilitation. For no matter how badly crippled a man is, the hospital regards it as vital that he be given all possible aid in rebuilding his life, mentally as well as physically, so that he can make some kind of contribution to the community in which he lives.

Erskine has always had a higher ratio of nurses to patients than any other hospital in the country because its policy has always been to provide 24-hour a day nursing care seven days a week. Three shifts cover each 24-hour period. In addition to old age and missing limbs, residents may suffer from diabetes, multiple sclerosis, pulmonary diseases, epilepsy, heart failure, asthma, arthritis and many other ailments that afflict us vulnerable humans.

Even Registered Nurses have to have some extra skills in Erskine, where most of the residents are elderly. A continuous programme of training tells them how to understand the men and women they care for and what made them they way they are. "Our nurses have to appreciate the traumatic change of lifestyle and the loss of independence a man experiences when he goes into a home", says the Director of Nursing. "He may be leaving his family where he was an authoritative father figure, or his job or his business. It may take time for him to adapt to hospital life. All this is why we try to provide as homely a routine and atmosphere as possible and help a man to retain his dignity".

Training takes in skills like how to manage aggression, violence, outbreaks of temper, how to move disabled residents, take blood samples, care for dementia patients, infection control, care of wounds, male catheterisation, palliative care for the dying and many other techniques.

In his report for 1991 the chairman, Admiral Tom Baird, said, "One of the more enduring traits of the hospital has been the historic low turnover of staff with its attendant advantage of continuity and know-how. A good example of this long service is highlighted by the retirement in January this year (at the age of 72) of our Steward, Alex Tomlinson. Alex came to the Hospital as a patient during World War II, married Sadie his nurse in 1946 and from 1951 lived and worked within the Hospital for 41 years in various capacities – the last 14 years as Steward. I wish them both a very happy retirement in their estate cottage and thank them for their contribution to the work of the hospital".

In January 2001 it was announced that 110 staff members would be receiving long service medals over the following weeks, a significant number for 15 or 20 years' service. Among the medal winners was Iain Grimmond, a chartered accountant who came to Erskine from a Glasgow accountancy firm in 1979 as Assistant Treasurer and became Treasurer (subsequently renamed Director of Finance) two years later. Bill Gordon, Estates and Facilities Manager, completed 20 years in September 2001. Bill is responsible for the vital task of keeping all the plant and equipment in good running order, repairs, purchasing of stores and a variety of other tasks.

All nurses are special, as so many of us have good reason to know, but Erskine's nurses are a race apart. "Like any other nurses they like to be recognised and rewarded for their work but their main motivation is the nature of their work, not how much they get for doing it", said Mrs Maureen Lundie, who retired from the post of Matron in 1999.

"Erskine is unique; the whole philosophy and atmosphere of the place is different from any other hospital", she told me. "There is a camaraderie among the staff and patients which is absent in other hospitals where staff and patients come and go, and where everyone is too busy to get to know anyone well".

"I know it sounds a bit hackneyed, but we really were like a family. Not only did we know the patients but we also knew every member of their families. We shared the families' joys as well as their sorrows. We went to football and rugby matches, theatre nights, shopping trips, concerts and other social events with the patients and even had a great sing-song on the hospital bus. All this made us very different from other hospitals.

"I was also careful to emphasise to the staff that the sick or infirm man in their care was not just a name on a chart but someone's husband, father, or brother, and was entitled to be treated with consideration and respect, in fact just the way they would treat their own father or brother. If you take away a man's dignity and respect he has nothing".

Mrs Lundie's comment on being awarded the OBE in the Millennium Honours List was "The honour was to work for Erskine". Maureen Lundie came to Erskine as a nursing officer in 1975. Two years later she succeeded Miss Mary Cameron, a former Major in the Queen Alexandra's Royal Army Nursing Corps, who was Matron for 12 years. When she retired in 1999 Mrs Lundie described her 22 years at Erskine as the most rewarding of her 45-year career. Such is the loyalty of nursing staff at Erskine that there have been only six Matrons since 1916.

Maureen Lundie was one of the first people at Erskine to campaign for the admission of ex-Service women, although at the time this was impracticable because there was no suitable accommodation or facilities and there had not been a demand for places, partly because women could look after themselves at home better than men.

From time to time women were admitted on a temporary basis but eventually the necessary accommodation and facilities became available to take them in on the same basis as the men, and the first woman to be admitted, in April 1980, was Mrs Elizabeth Watson, a 73-year-old former member of the Auxiliary Territorial Service from Elderslie. She died only a month later.

Another early patient was Squadron Leader Maisie Faith, who died aged 87, in 1999. Now there are seven women residents, the oldest of whom is 88-year-old Mrs Mary Childs, who was admitted in May 1999. She was formerly in the Territorial Army. Mrs Childs told me she would be happier if she were able to be more active, otherwise she is content with life.

A total of 469,000 women served in Britain's Auxiliary Forces during the Second World War. There were 21,300 in the Auxiliary Territorial Service (ATS) manning anti-aircraft and searchlight sites, and 182,000 in the Women's Auxiliary Air Force, the WAAFs, who served mainly on airfields in the UK. Smaller detachments were sent to the Middle East, India and the Pacific. A further 74,000 were called up for the Women's

Royal Naval Service, still known as the Wrens. There were about 17,000 women in the Services in the year 2000.

Mrs Lundie and one or two others took the view that if any of these women became ill and needed looking after they had the same right as the menfolk to good medical and nursing care. "There was never any ban on women at Erskine", says Dr Tom McFadyen, Director of Medical Services since 1978. "There just wasn't the appropriate accommodation and the necessary degree of privacy. After all, the hospital was built specifically for men. Besides, there were no applications from women for many years".

The present Director of Nursing is Mrs Lorraine Ross, who was appointed in the autumn of 1999. In June 2000 she was congratulated by the Executive Committee on gaining a bachelor of science degree with honours in Gerontological Nursing at Paisley University. She also holds a BSc degree in Health Studies from Glasgow Caledonian University. Mrs Ross and her husband Iain and their two children live in Glasgow.

"It didn't take long before I stopped feeling like the new girl at Erskine", she said. "From the first time I walked through the door I had a wonderful welcome from everyone, making me feel a part of the vibrant atmosphere that is Erskine. Everyone and everything appears to be so alive and happy I could not fail to feel part of it. Our residents really live a full life".

Sister Pat Constable retired from Erskine in February 2000 after 20 years' service, the last six as manager at Dunoon Holiday Home, and was succeeded at Dunoon by Mrs Jean Ward. Mrs Constable told me that if she was asked to give a newcomer to the hospital advice she would tell her, "A man or woman coming to Erskine is not just a patient. You have to try to understand the patient's whole personality, inclinations, needs, likes and dislikes, and his or her family background".

"You also have to understand the patient's family. Sometimes they feel guilty about putting Dad or Uncle Jim or Mum into full-time care with someone else, and you have to help the family dispel any guilt they may have. And of course you have to assure them that they can come and see their loved one any time".

Mrs Constable was one of the Erskine nurses who married a patient. Her husband Bert, a former Royal Scots Fusilier, lived at Erskine from 1947 until his death in 1986. Mrs Constable worked at Erskine for about 14 years and agreed to take charge at the hospital's Holiday Home in Dunoon until she retired. In the years before Dunoon opened she was one of the nurses who took patients twice a year to the Perthshire holiday village of Strathyre for a three-week holiday at the Order of St John's complex for the blind, which Erskine rented, but staffing costs for 24-hour care were high and the location was a bit remote.

Sister Ann McGowan, formerly Night Duty Manager, was Erskine's longest-serving nurse until she retired in April 2001. Her first day, January 16, 1974, is deeply engraved in her memory. "There was a Burns supper in full swing when I arrived in the evening and the night sister told me to go to Invernairn (Ward) but not to walk through the Gallery. I thought Invernairn was a place up north somewhere and I had no idea what the Gallery was".

"There were about 70 men in the Permanent Residents' Quarters and as the night progressed they got more and more merry. By 10 o'clock I was asking myself why I had left the Southern General to come to a place like this. I must have been off my chump. I told myself to stick it out and I would be OK and I've been OK ever since", she said, gurgling with laughter.

Asked what had kept her at Erskine 26 years she said, "I just love the place. It's a difficult thing to explain. Erskine is just not like anywhere else. Once in the early days I had to rescue a sheep from a septic tank. The sheep had been trying to save its lamb, which unfortunately drowned in the tank. There was a shortage of staff at that time and we all had to muck in and help each other". Another long-serving member of the staff was Mrs Margaret McCreery who started work at Erskine in 1943 as an office junior in the workshops and retired as a cashier in the Finance Office staff, and a grandmother, in 1993.

Tom McFadyen told me, "This place gets to you. It's a marvellous place to work in. The whole atmosphere is one of caring. The staff care for the patients and the patients care for the staff. I have been told more than once by a patient, "It's time you had a holiday", or "aren't you supposed to be off today?". And as others have undoubtedly told you, we're a family. We get to know the patients and their families so well that when I lose a long-time patient I am just as upset as anyone else".

Dr McFadyen took over from Dr Jack McCall, who had been Senior Medical Officer for 28 years. Tom had been doing some consultancy work at Erskine for about three months before he joined the staff. Nowadays he is assisted by five Bishopton general practitioners who visit the nursing homes daily. Night emergencies are handled by Medic-Call in Glasgow.

Many of Erskine's nurses come from surrounding towns and villages, Paisley, Erskine town, Bishopton, and Clydebank. Their loyalty is further evidenced by the fact that they have to make their own way to the Home by bus, which is not always easy because the Home is a bit isolated and bus services are not all that good.

There was something else that concerned the Matron and one or two others; the fact that most of the residents came from the West of Scotland, whereas men from Edinburgh, Dundee, Inverness, Aberdeen, Perth and other parts of Scotland were just as deserving but understandably didn't want to come to somewhere where it would be difficult for their wives or other family members and friends to come and visit them. There was also the fact that 40% of donations to Erskine came from outside the Strathclyde area. Thus was born the idea of taking Erskine care Scotland-wide.

Dr McFadyen was another who talked years ago about mini-Erskines in other parts of the country although he had one or two reservations. "I felt we didn't have the money to provide the standard of care available in Bishopton. I didn't want to see this standard lowered in any way".

The nurses and other members of the staff have raised considerable sums of money for the hospital over the years by taking part in wheelchair marathons, karaoke sessions and a variety of other activities. One karaoke night in Morton Hall raised £800.

Sisters Isobel Duffy, Christine Winter and Cindy Murray dressed in old soldiers and nurses uniforms in the early 1990s and went to public houses in Bishopton, Langbank, Bridge of Weir, Houston and Johnstone and sang old wartime songs. Mr Gordon MacPherson, Managing Director of a family business, whose wife Jane works in Occupational Therapy, went as a "bearded nurse". They did this on three successive Hallowe'ens and raised between £300 and £400 each time. The "can-carrier" on these expeditions was Dr Tom McFadyen.

Mrs Murray and 19 other nurses and 20 residents took part in marathons in the 1980s and 90s. The nurses pushed the wheelchairs more than 20 miles from the hospital to Paisley and back, led by the hospital wheelchair bus playing taped music which filled the streets. "We had wee buckets that people threw money into", she told me. "It was a wonderful public relations exercise because everyone knew where we were from and they stopped to talk to us. Residents' families also took part. My husband Jim and my children helped, too. Eventually the police asked us to stop the marathons because we were disrupting the traffic!".

"After that about five of us took part in the Glasgow half-marathon but it was very difficult because it was hard to push the wheelchairs up hills and we got left behind and felt isolated so we didn't do it again. We also held fêtes in Morton Hall and the wards had stalls selling tea and cakes and bric-à-brac.

"The staff's families took part in these and we raised a lot of money. There's not a lot of hospitals that do this kind of thing. If you like working with elderly people there is no better place than Erskine. There is just no point in going anywhere else to work". Mrs Murray has been with Erskine more than 20 years.

Bobby Steele has run seven 26-mile marathons and "countless" half-marathons since 1984. Keith Taylor has run three half-marathons and planned to do another three in 2001. Another regular runner in aid of hospital funds is Tommy Wiseman, a porter. Bobby and several other members of the hospital's hierarchy travel throughout Scotland each year giving talks about the hospital to Rotary clubs, British Legion branches, church groups, bowling clubs, youth organisations, Probus clubs, Army, Navy and Air Force organisations and anyone else who will listen to their fascinating story.

A member of the hospital's Executive Committee who took particular interest in the nurses' welfare, pay and conditions was Brigadier Alastair Pearson, Chairman of the Medical Committee. Even when he retired from the Vice-Chairmanship of the hospital on his 80th birthday in 1995 his interest in the hospital continued unabated.

In 1991 General Sir Peter de la Billière, Commander of the British troops in the Gulf War, was the guest of honour at the official opening of a new wing, incorporating the 30-bed Pearson Ward, named in honour of Brigadier Pearson who had worked so long for the hospital. The first stage of the new wing had been opened in December 1990 by a resident, John Picken, on his 100th birthday.

John was a former Warrant Officer in the Royal Scots Dragoon Guards. His son David flew from Canada for the event. Officers of the Royal Scots Dragoon Guards, who were serving in the Persian Gulf, and from the Blues and Royals, part of the Household Cavalry, were also there. He was one of four residents who have celebrated their hundredth birthday at the hospital. Mr John McDevitt, formerly of the Highland Light Infantry, was 100 in 1992, ex-Sergeant Edwin Turner celebrated his centenary in April 1995 and Mr James Aitken was 100 in May 1996.

The £2 million wing included a multi-purpose games room and dayroom extension. The money had been raised in just over a year after Prince Charles helped to launch a public appeal on behalf of the hospital. The games room was named The MacRobert Games Room in recognition of Lady MacRobert's munificence.

A cheque for £100,000 from the Trust was presented to Vice Admiral Sir Thomas Baird, Chairman of the hospital, by Lieutenant General Sir Robert Richardson, the Trust administrator. Mr Carroll Macnamara, Chairman of the Roehampton Hospital Trust, another Erskine supporter, handed over a cheque for £40,000 and £4,000 came from the nursing staff of Erskine Hospital.

When Brigadier Pearson died in 1996 as an Honorary President, the nurses of Erskine raised £5000 to establish the Erskine Hospital Alastair Pearson Memorial Award to demonstrate their affection and regard for the man who had cared about them for many years. This was not enough to generate enough interest to make the award worthwhile so the hospital executive gave a grant to bring the sum up to £10,000. The award is administered by The Tullochan Trust, which was also set up after Alastair's death to carry on his interest and commitment to the youth of Scotland.

The award is presented to a person aged 10-25 who has shown great courage over a long-term period to overcome extreme personal difficulties, or a person who has shown great selflessness over a period in caring for someone else.

Alastair raised the 15th (Scottish Volunteer) Battalion Parachute Regiment (TA) in 1947 and commanded it for six years. In 1944 while he commanded the 8th (Midland Counties) Battalion Parachute Regiment he met Joan Niven, a young war widow. They set their wedding day for June 8, but Alastair couldn't tell his bride-to-be that two days earlier he would be leading his battalion in the D-Day landing on Normandy. The couple were married when the battalion returned to Britain in September.

Alastair's heroic adventures in France earned him his 4th Distinguished Service Order and the nickname "Monarch of the Woods". He was also a Companion of the Bath, an OBE, and holder of the Military Cross.

In 1989 the Prince of Wales, Colonel-in-Chief of The Parachute Regiment, wrote in a foreword to a book about Alastair, *A Fierce Quality*, by Julian James:

I am delighted to write a Foreword to this book covering the deeds of one of the great leaders of the Second World War... His exploits are legendary, as must be indicated by the many decorations awarded to him in the field for out-standing leadership and conspicuous gallantry. Although the book concentrates on his wartime exploits, I am glad that it also refers to the outstanding services that he has offered to the Territorial Army, the Army Cadet Force and the famous Erskine veterans' hospital.

More barbecued
chicken legs, please

Food is fundamental to our existence and something we should enjoy. Miguel de Cervantes, of *Don Quixote* fame, wrote about 400 years ago, "Blessing on him who invented… the food that satisfies hunger". Not everyone is quite as appreciative of the people who prepare it for our dining tables.

A man in the next bed to me in hospital (not Erskine!) once asked a doctor, "Please may I have my operation before lunch", commenting that even surgery was preferable to the food served. Perhaps an exaggeration, but it is true to say that hospital food has been the butt of jokes since the first hospital. But not at Erskine Homes. Every possible effort is made to give residents interesting, nourishing and adequate meals, prepared as far as possible the way they want them, which is no easy task for so many residents.

Erskine's food bill for its residents is about £20,000 a month. The staff have their own dining rooms where they pay for their meals. The kitchens employ a total of 37 people, which includes five chefs and 24 catering assistants.

Dr Tom McFadyen negotiated a contract with the Community Dietician Service in nearby Paisley, which requires dieticians to service the home on a regular weekly basis. "The dieticians see the residents, keep a close watch on menus, train our staff members in all aspects of nutrition, all to ensure that no-one is under-nourished in any way", he says.

At one meeting of the home's welfare committee, at which all the Houses are represented, the Head Chef announced that the Catering Department was conducting a survey on residents' food preferences and requirements. Every resident would receive a form to be completed and returned to the Catering Department.

The Director of Nursing asked the ward representatives to stress to their fellow residents that the staff wanted to build their service around what the residents wanted and needed and were anxious to hear residents' views, favourable or unfavourable. Ward representatives have no hesitation in reporting to the Welfare Committee their fellow residents' comments on the food. Here is an extract from a typical report of the welfare committee.

Lauder Thomson Ward:
> Request for more variation at teatime. Too much pork and macaroni, and pies too hard.
> Advised that kitchen is having a problem getting good pies.
> Small sausage rolls are very much enjoyed.
> Request for beetroot. Advised by Head Chef that this is always sent to wards in a separate container when salad is served.
> Action: Catering Department

Invernairn Ward:
> Trial of sachets of sauce, salt, sugar, etc. not very successful as some residents have to get staff to open them for them.
> Action: Catering Department.

Permanent Residents' Quarters:
> Request that barbecued chicken legs be served more often.
> Representative complained that he had not seen any morning rolls for a while.
> Head Chef advised that because of late delivery morning rolls had not been ordered for the last three months. Chairman tasked Head Chef to find a supplier who could deliver early enough.
> Action: Catering Department.

The catering staff are unfazed by the many demands made on them. Michael Jones started as a hospital porter 22 years ago and is now Head Chef. Brian Fleming has been in the department 17 years and his father was in the department 33 years. Brian came into the hospital to cover the summer holidays and never left. Ian Milliken, Assistant Chef, had been there 39 years until he retired in October 2000.

Another important service to the patients is the Laundry which goes full blast much of the day, laundering vast amounts of patients' bedding and personal clothing. Mrs Julie Crowner has been doing this work cheerfully for 25 years. Her husband Bobby, a driver, has been with the hospital 16 years.

An evening with
Eddie Hunter

No matter how many activities are organised for residents, or trips away from the hospital to football and rugby matches, theatres and the like, or the availability of television and radio 24 hours a day, there is no substitute for visitors with whom residents can have a quiet and relaxed chin-wag. Erskine has always been fortunate in this respect as many individuals have turned up to have a talk with or entertain residents over the decades.

Relatives and friends of residents are, of course, the most frequent visitors, but there are also visits by members of the Westminster and Scottish Parliaments, local councillors, business leaders, residents of nearby towns and villages, groups from Glasgow, Edinburgh, Aberdeen, ex-Service organisations and many others.

For more than 60 years, for example, Erskine was visited on the second Tuesday of every month by members of the staff of Glasgow Post Office, a record that must surely be unique in hospital annals anywhere.

Girl workers of Ferguslie & Anchor Mills not only provided concert parties, but gave every resident ex-Service man a 10 shilling note at Christmas. For 30 years members of the Glasgow Jewish Branch of the Royal British Legion, Scotland, and the Association of Jewish Ex-Service Men and Women of Scotland visited Erskine at least once a year to meet residents and distribute gifts. Kincaids of Greenock and the staff of Buchanan's Black and White Whisky were also enthusiastic supporters.

Sir Harry Lauder brought a concert party to Erskine on a memorable winter's night in 1929. Sir Harry himself commanded the stage with a performance that must have taxed him emotionally more than his audience knew. For on 28 December 1916, only two months after Erskine had opened, his only son, Captain John Lauder, had been killed in France while serving with the Argyll and Sutherland Highlanders. (See page 96)

The cast of Scottish Television's *Take the High Road* entertained residents at Christmas 1985 and in August 1986 men of the Ghurka

Military Band gave a concert at Erskine and met Colonel Hamish MacKay, a resident, who commanded the 4th Ghurka Rifles during the Burma campaign of the Second World War. He won the DSO and was seriously wounded during the recapture of Mandalay from the Japanese.

In January 1987 the cast of the Pavilion pantomime Dick Whittington put on a show for residents, who included 91-year-old John Kelly, a Highland Light Infantryman in the First World War.

In more recent times there have been visits by The Heather Belles, a Ladies Pipe Band all the way from Canada, serving members of the Royal Navy, Royal Marines, Army and Royal Air Force who toured the hospital to chat with their ex-Service colleagues, and children from local schools brought smiles to the faces of everyone with their concerts and plays.

A visitor to the new Erskine Home just before the official opening in October 2000 was 83-year-old Mr Crawford Lemmon, who was born in the stable block in 1917. He told me he often drove over to the hospital with his wife Sheila from their home in Helensburgh to "see how things are going".

Mr Lemmon's father lost a leg in the First World War and was one of Erskine's first patients in 1916. After convalescence he worked on the estate as an electrical engineer. Mr Lemmon's brother Herbert and his sister Ethel were also born in the stable block, which was rather a misnomer as the block was used for accommodating patients and their families. The Lemmons left Erskine in the mid-1930s to live in Helensburgh. Crawford Lemmon later served in the Merchant Navy for 18 years.

Mrs Margaret Lawrie, now 86, has for some years been giving the "boys" in Yarrow Ward a party to celebrate her birthday.

Apart from the regular committee meetings at the hospital, a practice that has been retained throughout the decades, is the monthly visit by three or four members of the Executive Committee to wards and other sections of the hospital. The visitors make notes of whatever they think needs attention and report it to the hospital secretary who in turn puts it in the minutes of the next Executive Committee meeting for the information of members.

The theory is that the visitors may see something that has escaped the eye of the staff, but in fact there is very little that the staff do not know about. Nevertheless, the visits often result in something being fixed or improved sooner than it might have been. In May 1920 a visitor commented that "the kitchen should have some composition on the floor; the stone is too hard for those employed there". I have no doubt something was soon put down to make it easier on the feet of the kitchen staff. In March 1934 it was noted that "repairs to paintwork are becoming increasingly required".

Useful suggestions by the monthly visitors continue to be made to this day, although now and again comments do not add a great deal to the sum total of the world's knowledge: "The visit took place on a bright sunny day" or "The officer in charge clearly enjoys her job" or "The patients all seemed happy and content".

A visitor of a different kind to Erskine Mains shortly after it opened was Mr David Green, a Yorkshireman, who came to see a former army mate, Hugh Currie, whom he hadn't seen since 1950 when they were in the 8th King's Royal Irish Hussars. Mr Green had contacted numerous Service organisations over the decades in his search for his old friend. Finally he tried the Korean Veterans' Association in Aberdeen who put him in touch with *The Voice of Scotland*, a publication that helps to find people.

"Within a week of placing an advert someone from Dunoon phoned me to say they knew where Hugh was", said Mr Green. "I got the address of Erskine Hospital and phoned to ask if he was there. The first thing he said to me on the phone was, 'Do I owe you money?'"

A comprehensive programme of outings for Erskine residents includes football and rugby matches, canal boat trips, 10-pin bowling, ceilidhs, theatre visits and the Edinburgh Tattoo.

One of the more memorable outings took place in the autumn of 1986 when Mr Eddie Hunter, coach of Queens Park Football Club, invited a party of patients to visit the clubhouse at Hampden Park, the club's home ground. Two busloads of patients arrived at the clubhouse early on a Friday evening. Eddie had spoken to a few contacts to ensure there would be plenty to eat and drink. During the week, too, he had assured the Matron that the men would be home by 10 p.m. to allow the night nurses to get everyone settled in for the night.

The party in the clubhouse included members of Queens Park Social Club. Tea, sandwiches and "refreshments" were in plentiful supply. One of the Erskine men showed the gathering card tricks and some of the others started to tell their wartime experiences.

"Then a chap in a wheelchair asked if we had a piano so I wheeled it out and we had a lively sing–song", Eddie told me. "All the while I kept the lads' glasses topped up. Ten o'clock came and went, then 11 o'clock and I began to panic about what the Matron would say to me, but the men were enjoying themselves so I let them carry on".

"At midnight there was an insistent ringing of the doorbell and I found a policeman at the front door", said Eddie. 'Do you have a party of patients from Erskine Hospital here?' he wanted to know. The police-man phoned Erskine to reassure the Matron that the men were all right and that they would be sent home immediately".

"We managed to pour them into their buses somewhat the worse for wear by half-past midnight and away they went", said Eddie. "Next day I phoned the hospital to confirm that the men had got there OK and a nurse told me some of the men hadn't awakened until after lunchtime. I think it's fair to say they had had a good night!".

One of the more frequent and popular visitors to Erskine until a few months before his death in April 2001 was Jimmy Logan, who said simply, "If they ask me if I'm free, I say I'll make myself free". In October 1990 he organised a concert in the MacRobert Games Room to celebrate the hospital's 75th anniversary. A clip of the concert was shown on Scottish Television in the evening. Jimmy also narrated a promotional film for the hospital, which was shown to good effect throughout Scotland. Two later films were narrated by the actor and TV com-mentator Tom Fleming.

In 1990, too, Jimmy was appointed an Honorary President of Erskine Hospital, an honour that is not handed out lightly. He also had a wing in Erskine Mains named after him, which he popped into from time to time. He was made an OBE in 1996 in recognition of his contribution to the theatre.

One Sunday afternoon in 2000 I sat in Jimmy's comfortable lounge in Helensburgh and had tea with him and his wife Angela as he told me about his involvement in Erskine.

"My father joined the Scottish Horse at Dunkeld in 1917 and was sent to France, where they took the horses away from the soldiers and gave them bicycles because they found there was such things as machine guns, and horses didn't have much chance against them. Mind you, I'm not sure the bicycles were a lot better".

"Then they were made to replace the Scottish Infantry Regiments, which had been decimated. My father was transferred to the Seaforth Highlanders. On the 1st of January 1918 he was in a dug-out in Cambrai when there was a big German attack and my father was hit on the right leg by a piece of shrapnel from a shell. I saw the bit of shrapnel once. It wasn't much bigger than a tenpenny piece but it was enough to do a lot of damage and my father had to have his leg amputated in a military hospital there".

"He was shipped home and went into hospital in Newcastle where he had number of operations and then transferred to Erskine where he was fitted with a peg leg but later they developed a proper artificial limb and he had once of these fitted. By 1919 he was running his own concert party in Helensburgh and he spent the rest of his life in show business, but he was always so very proud of having been an 'Erskine man'. He considered that to be an accolade and it was because of what they did for my father and so many others that I took an interest in Erskine from an early age".

"Deeply embedded in my mind is the recollection when I was about 15 going up a stair somewhere in Sauchiehall Street. There were a number of wooden bunkers all round a room and inside were artificial right hands in one bunker and left hands in another and so on. I don't really remember if they had anything to do with Erskine or the Ministry of Pensions, if there was one, but they really brought home to me the horror of war".

Jimmy Logan's great hero was Sir Harry Lauder and in fact Lauder's piano sat only feet from where we sat in Jimmy's lounge. "When I was 12 I appeared in a wartime concert with him and when I was 17 he invited me to his home, Lauder Hall, and these memories formed the basis of a one-man musical I wrote called *Lauder*, he said. "For me, Sir Harry represented the best of my profession and there is no doubt that he was a superstar". Jimmy told me he once visited Captain John Lauder's grave in France because he felt it was something he should do.

A new Chairman

Lieutenant-General Sir John MacMillan retired from the Chairmanship of Erskine shortly after the opening of Erskine Home in October 2000 to try to resume the full-time running of his soft fruit farm in Stirlingshire. I say try because at the request of the Ministry of Defence he immediately took on the Chairmanship of Queen Victoria School, Dunblane for three years. The school is operated by the MoD and its 270 pupils are all the sons and daughters of Scottish and Scottish-based Services personnel. General MacMillan is also a Community Councillor and is involved with a cancer charity. And he was elected an Honorary President of Erskine in recognition of his work for the hospital from 1991 when he joined the Executive Committee so he can hardly be said to have retired from public service.

"If there is one thing that has impressed me greatly in my years with the hospital it is the dedication and enthusiasm of everyone connected with it, the staff, the members of all the committees who spend an enormous amount of time on the hospital's affairs", he said. "It is very inspiring".

Happily, the MacMillan family's involvement with Erskine did not end with the departure of General John, as he was affectionately known to the staff. His sister-in-law Jane, wife of George MacMillan, chief of the Clan MacMillan, who became a member of the Erskine Executive in 1966 at the suggestion of her father-in-law, General Sir Gordon MacMillan, still attends meetings. "He felt they needed some younger people on the Executive", she said, "and besides, I was a trained social worker and David Boyle, the Commandant, thought I could be of value to the Social Work Department of the hospital. I did part-time work there for 10 years and in that way I learned a lot about the running of the hospital".

Jane and her husband run the family estate at Finlaystone in Renfrewshire. Mr MacMillan, a former university lecturer, did not join

Erskine because his sight was not good, although he did serve on the board of Quarriers Homes for some years. Another Erskine worker is Mr Malcolm MacMillan, the Clan Chief's son, who has made a significant contribution to corporate fund-raising.

General John's successor as Chairman is Mr Mark Sherriff, CBE, Deputy Lieutenant of Stirlingshire, whose father Colonel C B Sheriff, was a member of the Executive Committee for many years until his retirement in 1966 when Mark joined the executive.

Mr Sherriff is also chairman of the MacRobert Trusts and a member of a number of smaller charitable trusts, a former officer in the Argyll and Sutherland Highlanders, former Honorary Colonel of the 7th/8th Argyll and Sutherland Highlanders, a Territorial Army officer for 30 years and chairman of the Highland Territorial and Auxiliary Volunteer Reserve Association for five years until 1996,

Mr Sherriff took his first meeting of the Erskine Executive Committee on October 18, 2000 after a farewell lunch for General John, at which the General announced that the ERSKINE 2000 appeal had reached its target of £5 million. Mr Jim Scott was elected Vice-Chairman of the hospital.

The new Erskine Home had been opened by Prince Charles a week earlier, the first residents were in the new 34-bed Erskine Mains Nursing Home, construction was proceeding on Edinburgh Erskine, the first bursaries outside Central Scotland were about to be awarded and the disposal of the Mansion House had been agreed with buyers, although still stuck with planning authorities. The old Nightingale[1] wards had become a relic of the past.

General MacMillan commented, "None of this would have been possible without the support of Erskine's many friends. I would especially like to highlight the part played by the powerful team of experts on the Executive Council, who have guided us through the complexities of planning, fundraising, construction and estate management, developing up-to-date care procedures and the many other disciplines that have formed part of the transformation of Erskine for the new century.

"We must not forget that running the new Erskine network will cost no less than the present operation, but our income from investments will be reduced after spending £26 million on the new buildings. We will therefore rely as much as ever on our sustained fundraising efforts after the Appeal closes, and I ask you now to remember your favourite charity in 2001 and beyond just as generously as you have done to date".

To the Erskine staff General MacMillan said, "Thank you very much indeed for maintaining Erskine as a flagship in the care of ex-Service men and women".

---

[1]So-called because of their similarity to the spartan wards of Florence Nightingale's time. Florence, who was born on May 12, 1820 established the Nightingale School for Nurses at St Thomas's Hospital in London, in 1860, the first school of its kind in the world, and thus founded trained nursing as a profession for women. She was prompted by her experiences in the Crimean War in 1854-56 when she was in charge of nursing in the military hospitals at Scutari, in Turkey, where she coped with conditions of crowding, inadequate sanitation, and shortage of basic necessities. She died on August 13, 1910.

The challenge

Erskine Hospital has been developing in one way or another since the day it opened and every Chief Executive, Commandant, Supervisor or whatever else he has been named, has had to oversee extensions, new building, adaptations, emergencies, dramas, visits by people of varying degrees of importance and pleas for more funds. But the most radical changes have been brought about by the hospital's efforts to cope with the new challenges and needs of a new century.

The task of overseeing the entry into the 21st century fell to Colonel Martin Gibson, who retired as Chief of Staff of the Army in Scotland at the at the age of 48, after 29 years' service, to come to Erskine in 1995. During his almost three decades in The Royal Scots, he had served at NATO headquarters in Norway, in the Falkland Islands and in Northern Ireland, among other places. He holds the MBE and OBE. His wife Lesley has been an enthusiastic fund-raiser since 1995.

The new Chief Executive had plenty of warning what he was taking on. The advertisement for his job said, "The Commandant will conduct negotiations with Central and Local Government Health Authorities, have a knowledge of marketing, be capable of liaising with the news media, and will oversee a multi-million pound investment programme to prepare the hospital for the next millennium". This was no exaggeration.

The first Supervisor at Erskine in 1916 was Lieutenant James Napier, a doctor. Colonel C A Gourlay, another medical man, was appointed in 1928. He was succeeded in 1940 by Colonel T H Scott. Then in 1950 Captain John Wentworth Farquhar, DSO, became Erskine's first non-medical Supervisor after a distinguished career in the Royal Navy.

Colonel David Boyle had been Commandant for nine years when I was elected to the Executive Committee in 1974, after about five years of part-time public relations work for the hospital. There were about 400 patients, and running costs were about £270,000 a year. The chairman was General Sir Gordon MacMillan.

Scotland's entire military establishment and everyone in the hospital was aghast when General MacMillan was killed in a car accident on January 21, 1986, on his way to Erskine. He had carried the hospital through 25 years of unprecedented change. His first major task was to complete the re-housing of the hospital from the remains of the war-time hutted accommodation into modern purpose-built wards. It was only appropriate that the hospital's most up-to-date ward at that time, completed in the mid 1970s, should be named after him as the MacMillan Ward.

In the latter years of General MacMillan's Chairmanship the hospital felt the full cost of the oil crisis and the subsequent wild inflation. To anybody who remarked to the General at that time that the likes of Erskine Hospital had served their day and that they should quietly fold up and accept defeat, his reply was resolute... "Erskine has a job to do and it will be here long after me". How right he was is reflected in the present confidence in the hospital and the services it offers, which are of a higher standard and greater range of provision than ever before.

It is a truism that no one is indispensable but there are people whose places are never filled in exactly the same way. General Sir Gordon MacMillan was such a man.

One of my early tasks as a member of the Erskine Public Relations Committee was to devise the launch of an appeal for £200,000 for a 26-bed extension to the hospital. I persuaded an old Glasgow Herald colleague, George MacDonald Fraser, a former officer in the Gordon Highlanders, to fly from his home on the Isle of Man to help to launch the appeal in the City Chambers, Glasgow. The money for the extension was raised in no time. George is author of the famous Flashman books and a Hollywood scriptwriter. I have always been envious of my old colleague, not only because of his success as an author, but because he wrote scripts for Raquel Welch.

David Boyle died in 1983 while still in harness. Without detracting from the virtues of any of the other Commandants before or since it is fair to say that he was immensely popular with everyone with whom he came in contact. He knew from personal experience what suffering was about having been a prisoner of the Japanese for three and a half years.

Mrs Jane MacMillan said of him, "He was a straightforward, sensible man, always genial, very caring and sensitive to people's feelings and needs. His relationship with staff and patients was always good. In fact he was he was one of the people who instilled the intangible but enduring Erskine feeling in people".

A block of three David Boyle Memorial Flats was opened by his wife Diana on August 17, 1983 as "the mark of a community's gratitude, of the hospital's affection and respect and of the grateful acknowledgement by many individual people of all that David Boyle was to them and of how much his life contributed to all who shared the healing of his companionship".

The need for this unique facility was identified by the Symposium of Scottish Ex-Service Organisations. The Royal British Legion Scotland undertook the fund-raising and Lord Haig launched the appeal. The flats are a memorial, not only to David Boyle but to the generosity of many people, charitable trusts, Service and regimental funds, and from individual and small groups. The block for many years also housed a hostel for non-resident workers in the workshops.

The popularity of the holiday flats was emphasised by Admiral Baird in his report for 1988. "The occupancy rate has continued to rise and the high number of repeat bookings is encouraging for all those concerned in the running and administration of this much-needed facility for the ex-Service community within Scotland and farther afield. The sliding scale of charges introduced three years ago has helped to increase bookings in the less popular months. One of the flats is now leased to Alzheimer's Scotland as a day centre.

With the cooperation of my long-time friend and colleague Tony Meehan of TMA Communications, who organises the very popular annual Scottish Press Awards, we established the David Boyle (Erskine Hospital) Memorial Award for the best series of articles on any healthcare subject. The awards ceremony is attended by the hierarchy of all the major Scottish news media and the hospital is mentioned in the awards list in every newspaper, some of them in far-flung parts of Scotland where Erskine Hospital is rarely, if ever, mentioned.

David's successor was Colonel Ken Shepherd, an Edinburgh man, who served the hospital for 12 years from 1983. On August 22, 1987, Ken and his wife Barbara went to a wedding reception in the Mansion House. The bridegroom, Captain Nigel Shepherd, was their son. Nigel and Captain Elizabeth Kerr of the Queen Alexandra's Royal Army Nursing Corps, were married earlier in the day in Erskine Parish Church. Three years earlier Colonel Shepherd's son Alastair also had his wedding reception at Erskine.

On November 8, 1995 Ken and Barbara, who was also an enthusiastic supporter of the Erskine, were piped out of the hospital on his retirement. Among the patients forming a Guard of Honour was former

Regimental Sergeant Major James Niblo of the Highland Light Infantry who had the job of making a soldier of Ken when he joined the HLI as a Private at Fort George, Inverness-shire, in September 1948.

"Aye, he was a good soldier – after a bit", 83-year-old James told me, "I am really sorry he is leaving. He's a gentleman". Colonel Shepherd's comment was, "They're a marvellous crowd and it will be a wrench to leave them, and the first class staff, but I will follow their fortunes closely", he says. And he does.

Colonel Shepherd's final appointment before coming to Erskine was Deputy Chief of Staff at Army Headquarters Scotland.

The future

A framed cheque for £3 13s 11d from the Central British War Fund, Shanghai, hangs on the office wall of Mr Iain Grimmond, Erskine's Director of Finance. It was delivered in 1989, 50 years after it was posted. Apparently a bundle of mail fell into German hands at the outbreak of war in 1939 and miraculously surfaced again half a century later in East Germany after the Berlin wall came down. Although this did not materially affect Erskine's finances it did come in a decade in which there was much anxiety about the hospital's future. In fact until fairly recent times the hospital's finances were often in a perilous state.

When Tom McFadyen became Chief Medical Officer at Erskine in 1978 he was told he might not have a job in six months' time because the hospital was so short of cash. "I took the job anyway and 23 years later I'm still here and I confidently expect to be here until I retire", he told me. A number of appeals for various extensions and improvements, coupled with publicity about the hospital's work, brought an increase in the number of legacies and donations.

"The development that put us on a firmer footing came in 1983 when changes in regulations allowed anyone in private nursing homes to claim Supplementary Benefit (later Income Support) from the Department of Social Security towards the cost of their care", says Iain Grimmond. "This had never happened before. A lot of our men had no money and consequently were not able to pay us much for their upkeep. They qualified for this benefit straight away. That brought in an extra million pounds a year from the Department of Social Security.

"An increase in donations and legacies also made our financial situation better. We were able to generate surpluses instead of deficits. After we had carried out vital repairs and maintenance, which we couldn't do before, we began to invest money, particularly in the late 1980s until the late 1990s.

"One could be led into thinking that money pours into Erskine from all sides and perhaps it does sometimes, but without the various organisations and individuals who support us, we would have a permanent annual deficit which would make it impossible for us to carry on", says Iain.

"All the appeals and donations over the decades have been vitally necessary to enable the hospital to meet its many commitments and to maintain its wards and other buildings and the services associated with these buildings. This support will continue to be vital especially as running costs of the new Erskine, Erskine Mains, Edinburgh Erskine and the Holiday Home in Dunoon will amount to more than £10 million a year".

When Mark Sherriff, a stockbroker, took over stewardship of the investments they stood at £1 million pounds. When he took over as Chairman in 2000 the value of investments was about £40 million. That was after £20 million had been realised to help with all the new buildings.

When I asked him if he was responsible for the remarkable growth of the investments Mark said with characteristic diffidence, "No, I wasn't, I merely gave advice. Other people provided the money". While it is true that there were many sources of income it is also true to say that without Mark's advice the hospital's reserves would not be in the healthy position they are today. Sir Michard Hirst now chairs the Investment Sub-Committee.

In April 2000 the Chancellor of the Exchequer gave a major boost to charities by extending the Gift Aid scheme to cover all donations by individuals who are UK taxpayers. By completing a simple declaration form donors can ensure that the charity will be able to reclaim tax of 28p for every £1 donated; therefore a donation of £100 is worth £128 to Erskine.

There are many statistics to illustrate the continuing need for Erskine Homes; until when depends much on what set of statistics one reads. All of them will be influenced by fluctuations in the population of Scotland, the tendency of people to live longer, the whimsicalities of national and local government policies, the economy of the country, developments in the National Health Service and a variety of factors yet unseen.

As already stated there have been a very large number of wars of one kind or another since the end of the Second World War in which British citizens have served. The nature of man being what it is, it is not likely there will ever be universal peace, and if Britain continues its traditional role as defender of the weak and oppressed there will inevitably come a time when our country's ex-Service people will need looking after.

The hospital's philosophy is well summed up in its mission statement:

...to provide best quality care to as many disabled ex-Servicemen and women throughout Scotland as is possible for as long as the need is there.

Martin Gibson regularly receives letters from relatives of residents which testify to the degree to which the hospital lives up to its philosophy. One such letter came in February 2001 from Mrs Sylvia Harris of Oxford whose father Jim Thomson was a Merchant Navyman for 10 years from 1938. Sadly, Mr Thomson died a few months after admission to the Home.

Dear Colonel Gibson
My father became a resident in Haig House last November. I am writing to express our thanks as a family for all that is being made available to my father as a resident at the new Erskine Home. From our initial enquiry last April we have been impressed by the professionalism and level of commitment of all staff whom one comes into contact with...Mabel in Admissions, Kate in Reception, nursing staff Miss Henderson and Isabel who were so helpful in the pre-admission process and Rita in Patient Banking and Mr Craigmil. Everyone could not have been more helpful or welcoming to me and to my relatives and friends who visit.

The staff in Haig House also deserve the highest praise and thanks. Their professionalism and personal integrity in dealing with human frailties is a lesson in humility; kindly, unhurried, humorous, very professional in medical matters and in addition to all that, supportive to me as Jim's relative knowing that I am at a distance and cannot just pop back which I would frequently like to do.

In Haig House the attention to detail in respect of giving the resident an identity, a name on the door, labels for clothes, dressing the resident in their own garments (not just anyone's clothes!) makes him/her feel special and still able to enjoy a quality of life; hot, nourishing, carefully planned food, well prepared and served. Since my father had his major surgery five years ago we have had many experiences of 'elderly in care', hospital, respite and longer term – and even the places thought of as having a good reputation. Not one attains the excellence and high standards set and achieved at Erskine. Several of them failed miserably in the most basic aspects of care of the elderly but fortunately for my father the experiences were short-lived.

The new buildings at Erskine are truly wonderful in all respects. It is the attention to detail that is so outstanding – a lot of light coming into the buildings, the dropped window sills to enable frail elderly still to enjoy 'life outside', the covered canopy at the front door for sheltering before enjoying an outing etc. and all the shared facilities such as the restaurant and other communal areas. It is a great tribute to the people who supported the appeal for the new buildings and to the staff who run it. The ethos of human kindness and the desire to provide the best is smiling out of every corner.

May I thank you on my father's behalf for this very special opportunity that has been made available to him and whilst he cannot initiate a thank-you himself, I know in his spirit he is very thankful indeed. Also for the generosity of the gift of £10 at Christmas.

My father was torpedoed in June 1940 from a "Q ship" off the Breton coast. There were few survivors and those who did survive were in an open boat with minimum rations for six days. Like many more who have endured such experiences, it is truly remarkable that the uniqueness of Erskine – offering a deep commitment to provide high standards of care, peace and tranquillity to elderly men and women who gave so much of themselves, when young – will continue into the 21st century.

With the sincerest of thanks from Jim's daughters – Sylvia Harris, Ardentinny & Oxford and Doreen Betts, Vermont, USA. Wishing everyone at Erskine a very happy 2001 and enjoyment of all the wonderful new facilities after a time of planning, moving and settling into the new environment.

Yours sincerely
Mrs Sylvia Harris

Doesn't that say it all?

Applications for admission to an Erskine Home, wherever it may be, may come from virtually anyone, the patient himself or herself, a member of the family, the general practitioner, another hospital, a service organisation or any interested party.

The patient then receives a visit from Erskine's Visiting Nurse to assess the patient's suitability for admission. This assessment is considered along with a report from the patient's GP, or in the case of someone from another hospital, the doctor in charge of the case.

If there should ever come a time when Erskine cannot continue the role it has played for more than eight decades, the hospital's care could be extended to widows/widowers of ex-Service personnel, or those who serve our country in some other way. In the meantime it is proud to do the job for which it was set up and whatever direction it may take in the future it will never be short of supporters if the people of Scotland can help it.

PRESIDENTS

Succeeding Lords Provost of Glasgow from 1916 to present time

Vice-President	Sir John Reid	1916-1933
CHAIRMAN	Sir Thomas Dunlop	1916
Vice-Chairman and Surgeon to the Hospital	Sir William Macewen	1916
Chairmen	Sir Harold Yarrow	1936
	General Sir Gordon MacMillan of Macmillan	1955
	Sir Eric Yarrow	1980
	Vice-Admiral Sir Tom Baird	1987
	Lieut General Sir John MacMillan	1995
	Mr Mark Sherriff	2000

SUPERINTENDENTS

Lieut J Napier	1916	
Col C A Gourlay. Physician	1928	
Col T H Scott	1940	
Capt J Wentworth Farquhar	1950	
Col David Boyle	1965	Commandant
Col Ken Shepherd	1983	Commandant
Col Martin F Gibson	1995	Chief Executive

MEDICAL OFFICERS

Dr W J C Watt	1916	Resident Medical Officer
Dr John Murray	1950	Resident Medical Officer
Dr James McCall	1951	Resident Medical Officer
Dr Tom McFadyen	1978	Director of Medical Services

In addition to the above the hospital has been fortunate in having many distinguished medical men and women as consultants over the years. Some of them also served on the Executive Committee. The hospital has also had as Honorary Presidents the Lords Lieutenant of Scottish cities and counties, high-ranking military men and others interested in the hospital.

CONTRACTORS

ERSKINE HOME: Main Contractor: HBG Construction Scotland Ltd.
Architect: Building Design Partnership

ERSKINE MAINS HOME: Main Contractor: Tulloch Construction Ltd.
Architect: Anderson Christie

ERSKINE EDINBURGH: Main Contractor: Barry D Trentham Ltd
Architects: Hurd Rolland Architects, Project Managers: W S Atkins Scotland
Consultant Architect: Mike Thornley

Index